Fast Eddie & The Gang

By
Herb Boldt

1

Fast Eddie & The Gang
By
Herb Boldt

Published by Herb Boldt
  406 Bridge St.
  East Tawas, MI 48730

Cover drawing by Don Herman of East Tawas, Michigan
Art Illustrations by Ed Sutton of Delton, Michigan

Interior layout by Kay Richey
Electronically created camera-ready copy by:
  KLR Communications, Inc.
  POB 192
  Grawn, MI 49637

Fast Eddie and The Gang / by Herb Boldt
Fishing / Hunting / Outdoor / Humor

ISBN 0-9748094-0-3

Dedication Page

This book is dedicated to Mary, my wife for more than 50 years. It was she who urged me to write "Fast Eddie and the Gang" and prodded me back to the computer whenever things were going slow or I had writer's block. Whatever the reason for wool gathering or other dalliance, Mary was quick to point me in the right direction. She also served as my editor and not once in the months it took to bring this book together was there ever a harsh word. Oh, there were a few "dangs" between me and her, but not between her and me. She proved to be the best editor (spelling, punctuation and context) that I have ever worked with. God bless her patience.

I also want to give a big thank you to Randy Jorgensen and Tom Campbell for allowing me to reprint the columns which first appeared in their magazine "Woods -N- Water News."

Table Of Contents

Introduction

Friends, neighbors and some family members have asked why I decided to write a series of stories about Fast Eddie and the gang. The answer is both simple and hard to answer. After more than 50 years of reporting and writing straight news for The Detroit News about murders, fires, Senate Crime Hearings in Washington and directing a staff assigned to me and writing a weekly outdoor column for the Associated Press, I was looking for a fresh start in a new field. Sort of: "Off with the Old; On with the New."

When I started to write for the Woods and Water News I chose to write in the straight format that popular national outdoor magazines have been publishing for eons. I know an eon when I see one and as a youngster I couldn't wait for my dad to finish his new outdoor magazines so that I could read them from cover to cover.

Over the years one of my favorite writers has been Patrick McManus, a renowned writer and wit for Outdoor Life Magazine for what seems like centuries — as opposed to eons. His column, "Last Laugh" appears near the end of the monthly magazine. I've always called him Patrick McManus until I met him at an Outdoor Writers Association of America Conference in Florida several years back. He was dressed nattily, not at all like I pictured him, but I told him his column was the first thing I read in Outdoor Life.

Remembering that conversation with McManus I thought "why not pattern my column after the great McManus." I have been a poor man's Patrick F. McManus ever since.

The gang, dating back to grammar school is led by Spunky Spriggs, the best woodsman, fisherman and outdoor cook I have ever known. The rest of gang consists of classmates Brad Morrison,

Skip Fisher, myself and a newcomer to the area, Fast Eddie Bresler, a southern born school teacher at our local high school.

Fast Eddie is the exact opposite of Spunky Spriggs and it is mainly his clumsiness and energy which I hope will bring a chuckle, and maybe a deep laugh occasionally. If it does, it will mean my decision to write about the outdoors with a sense of humor was a good decision.

I confess that for some reason it is difficult to write straight when sitting at the computer with a broad grin on your puss. Enjoy.

Herb Boldt

Southern Fishin' It's Not

It all started at a New Year's Eve party at Spunky Spriggs' place when my wife and I were introduced to Eddie Bresler, a new guy in the neighborhood.

"My friends call me Fast Eddie," were the first words out of his mouth.

Being a gracious host, Spunky brought us up to speed on Fast Eddie. He was born and raised in Florida and had never been out of the state during the winter until he took a job teaching science at the local high school.

"I never saw real snow until the week before Christmas," Fast Eddie advised.

"What do you think of it?

"What do I think of what?"

"Snow!" I almost shouted.

"Oh, snow. I think it's great, but I think you Yankees are crazy to move around so much in the snow. I'm just getting used to walking in it. I don't know how I'll ever learn to drive in it — the ice and snow, I mean."

Spunky led him over to another couple and we eavesdropped on the snatches of his description of snow and his motoring problems which included the time he had to be pulled out of a ditch.

Later in the evening Spunky and I were in the kitchen talking about our annual ice fishing trip to Lake Mitchell near Cadillac in Mid-Michigan. Fast Eddie walked into the middle of the discussion.

"I hope we get into the walleyes like we did two years ago," Spunky was saying at the time.

"Me, too."

Fast Eddie was mesmerized by the conversation and offered that he had never been fishing on ice. He asked what a walleye was. We described old marble-eyes and told him that the walleye was probably the best eating fish God created. Spunky told him we were going to fish for walleyes through the ice next weekend.

"You mean you fish on the ice? Don't you get cold?"

We probably exaggerated a tad about how nice it was standing on a wind-swept lake, chopping holes in the ice, setting up a shanty and jigging for walleyes.

"Fast Eddie looked puzzled at the word "jigging" and I explained the difference between jigging around a dance floor and jigging a bait up and down in an ice hole.

"Dancing sounds like more fun," he said.

Before Fast Eddie left the kitchen, Spunky invited Fast Eddie to join us for the weekend.

"Gee, I don't know. I'll have to ask Ellie Mae. I'll let you know this week."

"What did you that for?" I asked after Fast Eddie had walked away. "I know we catch fish, but you made it sound like we limit out on walleyes every time."

"Don't worry. He'll never go," Spunky said. "Remember, he's afraid of snow and ice."

Spunky called me on New Year's Day to ask if I had any extra clothing Fast Eddie could use on the weekend.

"You're closest to his size," Spunky said. I've got an extra pair of boots that I've saved since the 10th grade, but he needs some long underwear, snowsuit, heavy shirts, ice rod and anything else you can think of that he will need. I heard outdoor writers have a lot of that stuff hanging around."

"I'll let you know," I grumbled. "I still don't know why you asked him to come with us. We're going fishing to get away, not baby sit some Floridian who doesn't know a walleye from an Atlantic cod."

I could envision holding his hand all weekend and listening to him complain about the cold, about the accommodations at the motel, about the food at our favorite greasy spoon.

The last thing his wife said as we drove away was: "Don't let him fall into the lake."

On the drive to Cadillac I gave Fast Eddie a rundown on what we were going to do on the weekend and explained to him the art of jigging.

"It's important to impart the correct jigging motion," I explained. "The most effective way to jig the lure I'll let you use is really simple, and it's one of my favorite lures. You slowly lift the rod tip a foot or two and let the jig swim or fall naturally back to the bottom. It's a sure-fire system. In fact, any other method won't work."

I'll say this for Fast Eddie, he knew he was in the company of veteran anglers and asked a lot of questions. He thanked us after every answer and I had to exercise great control not to yell: "shut up."

Daylight was more than an hour away when we sat down to breakfast at a little diner that caters to fishermen and hunters. Even though the clothes on Fast Eddie were several sizes too big, he seemed to blend into the scenery quite well.

At the lake we piled everything onto our portable shanty and pulled it several hundred yards off shore to a weed bed that ran along the edge of a sand bar. There were several permanent shanties off the edge of the weed bed where we had caught walleyes over the years. We were glad it was a short walk because there was little snow cover on the lake and the ice was slick, except where foot traffic had roughed the surface a bit.

"Is it always this windy?" Fast Eddie asked. "Won't we get blown around?"

"No," I said "Our ice creepers will hold us just fine. Once we get the shanty up, we'll attach a couple of anchors and it'll hold just fine. The one fishing outside will be comfortable fishing downwind of the shanty."

Spunky drilled a couple of holes in the ice to match the two holes in the shanty floor while I began to assemble the shanty. I handed the rope attached to the shanty to Fast Eddie to hold while I fitted the canvas cover over the aluminum frame which was screwed to the floor.

"Don't let go of the rope," I told him.

Meanwhile Spunky cleaned away the ice shavings and we began to slide the shanty over the holes.

"I'll screw in the anchors and we'll get to fishing," Spunky said. "Hang on to the rope for a few more seconds while I anchor the shanty.

Just as Spunky bent over to pick up the two anchors a sharp gust of wind filled the canvas cover with air and it began to move across the lake. The shanty, not secured to anything but Fast Eddie, billowed out like a sail and began to move across the lake.

"Stop it. Don't let it get up any speed," Spunky yelled and grabbed for the rope in Fast Eddie's hand. He missed and the shanty began moving faster across the lake with Fast Eddie in tow, the heels of his oversized boots plowing two furrows along the ice. Spunky was 20 yards behind.

"Dig in your creepers," I shouted.

"He doesn't have any," Spunky yelled back.

It was quite a sight. Every time Spunky reached for Fast Eddie, the wind seemed to pick up just enough to keep Fast Eddie out of reach. All of the time this was going on, Fast Eddie was flapping one arm up and down and yelling something that sounded like —"Ya-hoo."

Two fisherman in one of the permanent shanties came out of their cocoon at the sound of the commotion. They agreed Fast Eddie sounded like a bronco rider, but looked more like a water skier. He even kicked up a small rooster tail whenever he slid through a patch of powdery snow.

I started jigging while Spunky and Fast Eddie walked back from the far shore with the canvas of the shanty now rolled up under Spunky's arm. The walleyes seemed to be off their feed.

Spunky and Fast Eddie were out of breath when they returned and it took the three of us some time getting the shanty cover on and the frame anchored to the ice. Spunky drilled a third hole and invited Fast Eddie to join me in the shanty He declined because he didn't like being cooped up..

I took the time to again demonstrate to Fast Eddie the proper way to jig before zipping up the shanty door. By that time Spunky was sitting in shirt sleeves and mopping the perspiration pouring from his brow, face and neck.

Ten minutes later Spunky said it was beginning to feel like old times when Fast Eddie called out: "What do I do now?"

I unzipped the shanty door and saw Fast Eddie standing over a walleye that was flopping on the ice next to his seat.

"Take it off the hook and bury it in the snowbank next to the shanty," I said. "Looks to be maybe three pounds. Good catch."

The next three walleyes Fast Eddie caught were about the same size. The five he got the next day were just a little over legal size. Spunky caught a two-pounder. I took pictures.

On the ride home Fast Eddie thanked me for showing him how to catch walleyes.

"My pleasure, I assured him halfheartedly. "What are friends for, but to show newcomers the proper way to jig for walleyes."

"I want to apologize for that — for not exactly following your instructions. After the crazy ride across the lake and the long walk back into the wind, I was sweating. That's why I wanted to stay outside — to cool off.

"Then I got cold and started shivering so badly that all I was able to do was shake the rod up and down and back and forth. That's when the fish grabbed the bait.

"I'll try to do it right the next time."

A Gang – Officially

When you live in the country and your next door neighbor lives more than a half mile away, it gets lonesome at times. That's probably why neighbors talk about, and are likely to remember, folks for some outstanding or unusual deed.

Surprisingly enough, downright stupidity, also gets you remembered. And the memory lasts nearly as long as a Herculean feat.

The incident I'm about to relate is Herculean. It was a case of Spunky being astute enough and strong enough to beat a pair of carnival roustabouts at their own tricks. It was something to be remembered. It was something to be talked about by folks in our rural community for decades.

Come to think about it, most of the sobriquets (aliases or nicknames) are awarded for Herculean feats, but not all.

Nobody could expect a Herculean feat from Fast Eddie Bresler. After all, he most often is referred to as the shy, but brilliant science teacher at the local high school. However, it is his reserved, backwards and bumbling style that most folks talk about.

They expect him to come up with something that comic strip characters might do every time they bump into him.

For Fast Eddie the words "bump into" are apropos and dates back years ago when he bumped into the same car at two different locations within a 15 minute stretch.

The only member of the gang who can be identified with Herculean feats is Spunky. Townspeople have been in awe of his strength since his senior year in high school when two tipsy carnival roustabouts picked on two of his buddies.

It happened at the County Fair. Spunky, Brad Morrison and I had gone to the fair. We were minding our own business when the two goons descended on Brad and me and began pushing us around, de-

16

manding that we fight them.

I wasn't worried, though, because I saw two sheriff's deputies moving toward us. Before they got there, Spunky rushed up, grabbed each of them by the shirt collar and held them up over his head.

They were kicking and screaming for help from the sheriffs deputies. The law officers must have been hard of hearing because they turned back toward the midway as soon as Spunky grabbed the pair.

Later that evening, several area people asked Spunky if he was the one who had punched out the two bullies.

"I guess so," Spunky told them. "I didn't do much. All I did was stop them from messing with my friends."

The story got around faster than the speed of light and next morning my mother asked if I had been in any fights at the fair. I told her what happened and the next thing I know she's on the phone to a neighbor telling her how Spunky had saved my life.

Spunky's stature grew overnight. He became the talk of the town. Folks, who before didn't care much for the Spriggs clan because they were dirt poor, actually went out of their way to shake his dad's hand and tell him what a fine son he had.

While Spunky's stature soared, my stature fell into the ditch. I became known as the guy Spunky saved from a bad beating.

I don't remember thanking Spunky for what he did, but must have because we have remained best friends since. However, I'd be less than honest if I didn't admit that his reputation for being able to do anything and everything and the guy who saved my life rankled me for 15 years.

The four of us — Spunky, Brad, Skip Fisher and myself — were called "the gang" because we all schooled together and pretty much stuck together whatever the season or the reason.

We were called the gang by classmates all through high school because we played sports together, fished together, hunted together and seldom were seen outside each others company.

But the term "gang" didn't become official until the school's disciplinarian, Sister Esmeralda, mentioned it while trying to find out who broke three school windows just before Halloween during our junior year in high school.

Her discussion led most of the kids in school to believe we were the villains.

She made an official apology to "the gang" in front of the whole school two days later when she discovered who the culprits really were.

Whatever, the four of us have been called the gang to this day. Spunky naturally assumed leadership of the motley crew. He lived up to his reputation as leader because he shot more game (the biggest bucks) and was a wizard with a shotgun, flyrod and spinning rod.

I felt smaller and smaller each year. I felt like I was his shadow. And then it happened.

We were deer hunting state land upstate. It was opening morning and I was on stand about 400 yards from where Spunky was sitting in the middle of a heavy thicket. About 8 a.m. I heard a shot from his direction. I thought there goes that eight-point we saw during scouting expeditions.

Ten minutes later I heard something crashing through the cover between me and Spunky. I turned to the noise and brought my rifle up to readiness. I thought it must be the biggest deer in the state because of the racket it made.

Suddenly I spotted a flash of a hunter's coat. Seconds later Spunky came into full view. He wasn't walking. He was running.

"You got to help me," he said calmly. "I think I broke my nose."

"How'd you do that?" I said before noticing the blood running down his face.

"That big eight-point come through, but because of all the brush I couldn't put my crosshairs on him. He sounded like he was going to run me over."

"You missed him?"

"Nah, I leaned sideways and poked the rifle under some low boughs. I had to lean far to the left. When I shot, the rifle bucked up a storm. It came out of my hands and the scope hit me in the nose. I think it's broken."

I told him I'd take him to the hospital.

He said: "Okay, but find Brad first and ask him to take care of my deer. I'll walk back to camp and wait for you there."

The doctor told him his nose wasn't broken, but that he'd have to stitch it, because the only way he was going to stop the bleeding was to put a dozen stitches across the bridge of his nose.

During the gang's ritual — toasting the successful hunter — I suggested that we keep Spunky's story our secret to protect his Herculean status.

We all agreed. A funny thing happened — all my rancor disappeared.

One Shot Eddie

F ast Eddie Bresler has been the most excitable person in the gang. He also has provided us with a lot of excitement over the years.

Like the time he trudged back to camp on opening day while the rest of the gang were finishing up lunch. He was out of breath and ignored us as he went to his truck and hurriedly stuffed a box of cartridges into his vest pocket.

Before his appearance we thought he was lost again because he never misses lunch.

When he started back for the trail Spunky Spriggs stopped him. "Where you going now? Lunch is ready, in fact it's almost gone," he said.

Fast Eddie slowed up long enough to tell us he had a fine buck tethered to a tree and had to come back because he had run out of ammo. He started off again, then stopped and asked us to go back and help him get his deer.

We collectively shrugged shoulders and followed him back to his stand, and sure enough, there was a buck tethered to a tree. It seems he had dropped the buck, put a rope around its neck and was dragging it to a more open spot in an orchard to field dress it when the deer suddenly stood up.

The deer was groggy and Fast Eddie was able to wind the rope around the tree three times and keep the deer where it was. He said he picked up his rifle, aimed at the deer's neck and pulled the trigger.

Click!

It was then he realized he had put the cartridges back in the truck instead of his pocket after racking the first shell into the chamber. He first tried to cut the deer's throat, but thought he might get gored and decided to come back to camp for more cartridges.

It was a good thing he brought more than one cartridge this time because he didn't finish the job until the fourth shot.

A science teacher at the local high school, Fast Eddie is not dumb when it comes to books and learning, but the poor fellow grew up in Florida and never hunted or fished much until the gang got hold of him a few years before this incident.

Fast Eddies wanderings are legendary. He may not score on a buck some years, but if he manages to hunt a full season — usually opening day and weekends — he's had a good year.

That may be the best Fast Eddie goof, but you'll have to decide if the topper of them all didn't come until a few years later..

That year, Spunky Spriggs, Brad Morrison, Skip Fisher, Roger White, a friend of Skip's and I figured we had a busy night ahead of us. The often lost Fast Eddie had not returned to camp. It was dark and we were eating our supper because we figured we needed the energy especially if it took the better part of the night to find him.

To complicate matters, Fast Eddie was hunting several miles away from camp on a piece of land owned by one of his fellow teachers at the local high school. A major complication was that we knew where the property was, but didn't have the foggiest idea which part of the large parcel of land Fast Eddie planned to hunt.

"We'd better hurry eating," I said as Spunky fired up the outdoor grill.

"No hurry," he said. "Do the rascal good to sweat it out a couple of hours. There's roads all around the place. He'll hear traffic and head for the road."

"Yeah, but knowing him he'll probably turn the wrong way and walk all the way around the section to the car 100 yards from where he came out," Roger said. "We hurry and find his car. That doesn't mean he's in the woods."

"That's right," Skip joined in. "Remember that time he was having a drink at the farmers over by Greentown. Good thing we didn't hurry out after him because the farmer brought him back to camp before we took off."

The steaks were done and we were filling our plates when Spunky said. "Hey, I hear a car. It's him, he's never had that noisy muffler taken care of. Get another plate."

Sure enough a few seconds later later Fast Eddie pulled into camp.

"Get lost again?" Spunky called.

"No, but I did get a nice buck. How'd you all do?"

"You got the only deer," Roger said. "How big?"

"Seven point."

"Let's take a look," Brad said.

"I want to eat first. I'm starved."

Fast Eddie told us how he had spotted the buck about 400 yards away standing in a woodlot.

"I watched the buck step into a cleared spot between the lines of trees. He started coming right at me. It was getting late and I kept looking at my watch to make sure it was still legal to shoot. He was walking down a line of pines. I was trying to pick a spot to shoot.

"With less than two minutes of legal time left he stood in an opening about 150 yards from me. I shot. I didn't see what happened to him, but I went up to check for blood. I got mixed up on which tree line he had been in and it took me several minutes to find the right spot and there he was lying dead as a doornail."

"Are you joshing us," Spunky said. "I don't see any blood on year hands."

"It was so late I didn't field dress it. Just dragged him out to the road, and hailed a group of hunters going by. They helped me toss it into the trunk. You'll all see it after supper."

When Fast Eddie had finished eating, we all went to his car to help him lift his deer out of the trunk.

"What's that noise?" Brad asked. "Sounds like it's coming from the trunk."

"You're hearing things," I said and leaned toward the trunk as Fast Eddie inserted the key.

The trunk lid popped open and a buck's head popped up in the glare of my flashlight.

All hell broke loose as the seven-point tried to get out of the trunk. Spunky ran back for his rifle, but the deer was out and gone by the time he got back.

We searched all of the next day trying to find Fast Eddie's buck without success. On the fourth day of the season and two days after Fast Eddie returned to the classroom, Brad dropped a nice buck a half mile from our camp.

There were two wounds on the deer. Brad's heart shot and the mark of a bullet which had gone through and through the top of the buck's backbone which apparently paralyzed him for a spell.

Fast Eddie had done it again.

Scam Game

June is normally associated with Father's Day, but let's not forget all of the graduation days in the same month and the money dad has forked out to help some relative or friend's kid get a start in college.

Let's see: there are your own sons and daughters, your brother's and sister's kids and for good measure we'll throw in a few gaggles of children of every day friends, bosses and neighbors to complete the picture.

Spunky Spriggs, Brad Morrison, Skip Fisher and I rarely mention graduation days. Come to think of it, our wives seldom mention them either. We all have had a bad experience with graduation day at one time or another and bad experiences are better forgotten.

It all started when our oldest, Milton, graduated from high school. He was only the third in my family to make it all the way through high school. I was the first, my sister, Eileen, was second and Milton was third.

I was looking forward to his graduation until Spunky mentioned at one of our gang meetings at the Slop Shop that graduation day was the first day of our annual pike fishing week.

"I'm sure glad my kid doesn't graduate this year," Spunky said. "Before Christmas I sent for our reservations and made a down payment on the rental of the two cabins on Big Pike Lake. I'm sure the gang hates to miss Milton's party, but the down payment already was made when I found out that Sunday was graduation day."

"Hey, wait a minute," I shouted. "Milton's graduating and I can't go. And I don't think my best friends should go either."

There was dead silence around the table. Not one of my best

friends would look me in the eye.

"Don't be sore, Herb." Brad stammered, "but we've got to go. I'll be on vacation from the shop. It's the best trip we make all year. Remember, last year I smoked three of the pike I caught. You should remember because you're the one who wolfed down most of the last one at the Christmas party.

"I like Milton, he's a fine boy and I'd be proud to have him as a son. He's also a fine fisherman and I know he'll understand if you miss his graduation and go on the trip with us."

"Count me out," I shouted. "And that goes for the rest of the things we always do together. I'd resign, but we don't have any gang amendments or rules that say I have to resign, but I resign anyway."

I slammed the door on my way out, but not before I heard Skip say: "He's really ticked."

The next three weeks were hell. I didn't have any contact with the gang. I didn't go fishing either because I was afraid I'd run into one of them on a trout stream some morning or evening.

I often drove past a local trout river and spotted one of the gang's pickups parked at the access site to the river. Each experience made my disposition fouler than it was. I even thought of trashing Skip's new vehicle one evening, but talked myself out of it.

I was busy however and I thank my wife for that. She saw to it that I chased down party favors, napkins and you name it during the weeks before graduation. I think I put a couple of hundred miles on the truck during the week.

Milton's graduation was great and my chest puffed out whenever he was awarded an honor, but I dreaded the party we planned for the afternoon. I also wondered how the gang was doing on Big Pike Lake.

The party, scheduled from 1 p.m. to whenever, got off to a quick start. Several neighbors arrived at the stroke of one and soon I was deep in conversation about the current drought, how the neighbor's crops were doing and what steps they were taking to keep the deer out of their fields.

I was sitting on the porch talking with Aunt Fannie (her name's really Frances and she's not my aunt, but that's what everyone calls her) about how lucky the kids of today were to get schooling instead of having to go to work when they're still babies.

She was in the middle of a story about her experiences in a one-room schoolhouse when I saw a cloud of dust coming down the road.

"I don't know why everyone has to drive so fast," I interrupted. "We best go inside and let the dust settle. You can finish the story later."

I was about to enter the door when I noticed the dust was being raised by not one, but three trucks.

"Hey, that's Spunky's truck," I thought to myself. "What's he doing here? He's supposed to be fishing."

Spunky, Brad, Skip and their wives greeted me with big smiles and a lot of noise.

"Why aren't you at Big Pike Lake?" I asked and felt better than I had for weeks.

"Later," Spunky said. "Where's the keg of beer?"

Each member of the gang avoided any and all conversation about the annual pike fishing trip until late in the evening — after all of the neighbors and casual friends were gone. When we got around to talking about fishing, it wasn't introduced casually.

"You going to be ready to go fishing by 4 a.m.?" Spunky asked.

"Go where?"

"To Big Pike Lake, dummy."

Spunky's answer brought a spate of back slapping and guffawing among my three friends which can best be described as nauseous.

"When I saw you I thought you had canceled the trip," I said.

My answer brought another outburst of laughter.

"Hey, I can be ready. In fact I'm ready to start packing right now."

"It shouldn't take you too long," Spunky said. "Your wife has your ice chest loaded with your share of the grub, and she's even baked a couple of cherry pies."

"My wife?"

"You're been had," Spunky said, "Had in spades. I checked the graduation date the first week of school and told the gang we couldn't go this year until Monday. They said okay, but let's not tell Herb. I called Homer and he's saving the cabins for us beginning tomorrow.

"Skip picks up the pool because he came the closest to how you would react to the news that we weren't staying for Milton's party. No hard feelings, I hope."

"I love you guys, but that isn't going to stop me from picking up all the bets on Big Pike Lake."

Somebody upstairs must have a soft spot for suckers who get taken in a scam because I caught 15 of the 20 pike we took during the week. And I've never let those low down bums forget it.

The Gavel Rules

There must be more than the average number of fly fishermen in the gang's corner of the world. However, it's difficult to count the number of fly fishermen in any area of the state, or world for that matter.

My guesstimate is based on the fact that the county the gang lives in has an unusual number of assault cases every year which involve persons arguing over fly fishing techniques or the worth of one fly over another.

For instance, in one case before Judge Emmet Emery, Harvey Smith, the local mortician, accused Snark Snodgrass, the town's only auto mechanic, of punching him in the nose during a debate over whether a Slate Wing Mahogany Dun is a better trout catcher than a Hendrickson.

The townspeople crowded the small courtroom for the trial and their sympathy clearly was with the defendant Snark. They definitely had chosen sides in the legal matter.

While they were sorry that Harvey had a swollen proboscis, they hoped it would heal a long time before anyone of them would need or want his services. However, no one, including Judge Emery, wanted the town's only auto mechanic to languish in the slammer and miss a few days work.

At trials end, Judge Emery rendered a decision fit for an appellate judge. He said the argument was over an unprovable subject and was frivolous.

He ordered Snark to cover the mortician's deductible insurance payment and demanded the mortician pay for the repairs to the auto mechanic's jacket which was torn during the fracas.

During the trial Judge Emery said he wasn't a fly fisherman, but often thought about trying it. He spent much of the court's time attempting to ascertain the fly fishing abilities of the two protagonists. That's where the gang got involved in the trial, or, maybe a better description would be the after-trial.

Years before the gang had built an Olympic sized bluegill pond behind Spunky Spriggs' barn. It was a natural place for a pond because a spring had been bubbling out of the side hill behind the barn for years. The water naturally sought its own level and made the ground at the base of the hill wet all year.

It was Spunky's idea to build a trout pond, and since the gang would be allowed to fish there, we all pitched in and helped. It took us a month. We dug the hole for the pond with a backhoe and used the dirt to build up the sides of the pond. The packed dirt made it look like there was a platform all around the pond. We topped the platform off by planting cattails and other wild plants to attract insects for the trout to feed on.

It took most of a summer for the pool to fill and Fast Eddie Bresler ordered some trout from a hatchery the following spring and we were in business. We watched the trout grow for a time, but eventually they all died off.

Brad Morrison and Skip Fisher, who helped build the pond, were cool to planting any more trout in it. They maintained that we ought to plant bluegills because they'll live anywhere.

After several noisy sessions, which landed just short of Judge Emery's courtroom, we decided to plant bluegills in the pond. The cost was negligible because the gang caught forty or fifty big bluegills during the next summer and dumped them in the pond.

The following summer we fly fished the pond and caught and released nearly every bluegill we had put into the pond and by the end of the next summer there were little bluegills all over the place. There were so many bluegills that we had to start feeding them and we introduced a couple of smallmouth bass in hopes of slowing slow down the population explosion.

That's when Spunky came up with the idea of starting a fly fishing school for a few of the local kids. We dredged up some ancient fly rods for the students to use and each of us recruited one teenager for fly fishing lessons.

Spunky explained what fly fishing was all about, demonstrated the art of placing a fly where you wanted it and then turned the kids loose. You never saw such a sight in your life. There were hooks caught in everything and everybody before the hour-long lesson was over.

We didn't lose a student all year and by the time the summer was over, the teenagers were casting like pros. We went to two classes a week the next year and kept the fly fishing school open for 10 more years and graduated more than 90 boys between the ages of eight and 15 and a score of adults. Two of the students were Snard and Harvey.

We opened the school for one more summer after the trial. We had to restock the pond with bluegills for our final student, Judge Emery. He was as eager, or more eager, to learn how to fly fish than the teenagers.

He bought an expensive fly rod and showed up for his first lesson looking like someone who just stepped out of the pages of an expensive sports catalog.

Alas, Judge Emery had everything in his favor except finesse. The poor judge handled the fly rod like it was a gavel.

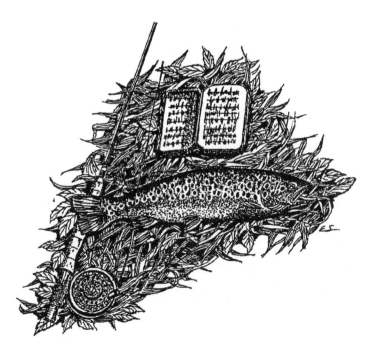

The Aliens Cometh

A small town never becomes famous, unless of course, an ax murderer is born there or one of its citizens becomes a governor or president.

The little town where our gang lives is like so many small towns across Michigan. A few local businesses, a school run by the nuns, a gas station, post office and four churches of different denominations.

I almost forgot the Slop Shop, a small bar, but I won't try to describe an assortment of buildings which cater to the arts and crafts people.

Our town has never spawned an ax murderer, governor or president, but it shared headlines in big city newspapers and on national television for a week. I don't think anyone in town escaped being interviewed, analyzed or offered a bribe to let the world in on our little secret.

During the "scare" the gang talked about selling everything we owned and trekking to Alaska and starting all over again.

However, the smarts which come with age, as well as a declining affection for work, overcame any fear and we stayed — shotguns and rifles in truck cabs during the day and next to our bed at night.

I'll never forget how it started. The gang, except for Fast Eddie Bresler, were assembled for our monthly get together at the Slop Shop. We were discussing trout fishing and trying to get Brad Morrison to stick to flies only on opening day.

"This is America," Brad pontificated. "I can fish any way I want. My God, there's a guy just came in who looks like Mike James' double. Only he's got snow white hair."

The sound of the Slop Shop clientele rushing toward the stranger ended Brad's soliloquy on opening day.

"Something's going on," Skip Fisher said. "I think it's Mike, but his hair was black when I talked to him yesterday about cutting some timber off my place."

We all turned toward the bar where Mike James was downing a triple something or other. His white hair glistened in the light of the hanging light over the bar. He held out the glass for a refill, downed it in one gulp and turned to the gathering crowd around him.

"Git your guns," he shouted. "Them fellers from outer space has landed."

"Hey, Mike, how many of them drinks do we have to down before we can see them fellers, too?" Ivan Snodgrass asked.

It took three patrons to pull Mike off Snodgrass who kept whimpering something about it only being a joke.

"You calling me a liar?" Mike asked, a defiant glare sweeping across the crowd.

Now Mike James is a bull of a man. He went to school with the gang. The day after graduation from high school he left to timber in Minnesota and Wisconsin. None of us had seen him until a couple of months before when he showed up at the Slop Shop.

He looked like he had just come in from the bush. His black hair was long and unruly and he had the look of a mountain man who'd fight anybody, any time, just for kicks. He told us he had come home to watch after his ailing mother.

"What's this all about?" the Slop Shop proprietor, Pete Scrim, asked when Mike had quieted down a bit.

All eyes turned toward Mike. He shoved the glass at Scrim for a refill and plunked down on a bar stool. He waited for his drink before beginning.

"I was walking back to the swamp to get a handle on deer sign when I heard a funny whirring sound. At first I didn't pay much attention to it, but it got louder and louder. It sounded like it was coming from that pasture that's nearly surrounded by the swamp.

"You know the swamp, the one out toward Cooper Road. I hurried over to see what all the racket was about. When I got to the edge of the pasture I saw something that scared the hell out of me and I ran to my truck and hustled to town to tell Chief Doyle what I seen. He wasn't in his office, so I came here."

"Stop wasting time. Tell us what you saw," I shouted.

"It was a space ship. You know like one of them flying saucers you see in the funny papers. It was a bright greenish yellow. It glowed and looked like a big dish. It was hanging above the pasture like it was ... like on a string or something.

"And so help me God, there was a little guy in the machine. At least I think it was a little guy because all I could see was his shape behind a kind of windshield. It was hard to see against the light, but whatever it was, it must have known I was looking at it because what I think was a face turned toward me .

"Then suddenly it went straight up in the air and flew across Old Man Gentner's barn and that's the last I saw of it. As God is my judge, that's the plain truth of what I saw. What should I do now?"

"Tell Chief Doyle, He'll know what to do," Scrim advised.

"Maybe he'll lock you up," someone whispered.

"I'll try to find him," James said and walked to the door.

He looked as sober as a judge.

Nearly everyone in the bar suspected he had been samplng some of the hooch he often manufactured in the swamp that borders the pasture where he claimed he saw the flying saucer.

All of the patrons, including the gang, stayed until closing arguing about whether Mike was sane, bombed out of his mind by his homemade hooch or (God forbid) telling the truth.

The consensus of those present was that they did not believe Mike's story.

However, Mabel Whatley, a 60-something stringer for the only daily newspaper in the county, fancied herself as a probing reporter since she was hired to keep editors informed about social events, school and township meetings and the like. The newspaper's job specs seemed to disagree with her personal idea of what the job was all about.

None at the bar that night paid much attention to Mabel, which is not unusual because few pay much attention to her on any night, or day, for that matter.

For years we had scoffed at Mabel and the aura of importance she attached to her stringer's job and laughed at her speeches about the power of the press. Yes sir, she took her job seriously.

None of that entered my mind that night as I walked past the pay telephone booth and saw Mabel hunched over the handset with her back to the door.

My wife, Mary shook me awake at 6 a.m. which normally isn't too early as I subscribe to the theory that the early angler catches all the fish.

However I hadn't fallen asleep until sometime after 4 a.m. And then I tossed another hour thinking about what Mike James had told the Slop Shop patrons about his seeing a flying saucer on his property early last evening.

My first thought upon hearing Mike's tale was that he was hallucinating, but hallucinations don't make your hair change from black to snow white in a day. Whatever Mike saw, or thought he saw, had made him look like Santa Clause overnight.

"What do you think of Mike's story?" Mary asked when I had come to some sense of awareness.

"It's 6 a.m. How in the world do you know about Mike's story?"

"The phone has been ringing all night," she replied. "Everyone I know called to ask what I thought because you were there. You must have drunk too much. I've been trying to wake you up for more than an hour, but all you did was moan."

An hour after incessant nagging I pulled the truck out of the barn and my wife and I started for town. I told her nothing would be going on, but she insisted. She also insisted we drive past Mike's place so that I could point out the place where Mike said he saw the flying saucer.

The dirt road was packed with parked cars. It looked like the whole town was checking out the story. I refused to stop, even after we saw more than 100 people tramping around the field in a light rain.

"So much for nothing going on," my wife commented.

The commotion bothered me because we planned to fish the creek at the rear of Mike's property on the opening day of the trout season in two weeks and I worried the sightseers would make the fish skittish for the next month or more.

In town we saw another group of people standing outside of the police station listening to Chief Doyle.

"Go home," he shouted to the crowd in front of the police station. "There's nothing to see, nothing new. I've just started to talk with Mr. James. Now go home. There's no danger, but you'll be safer at home."

With that Chief Doyle slammed the door shut and disappeared inside. We went to the local restaurant for breakfast. It was the first time we had to wait for a seat. The place sounded like a convention of wild turkeys — each trying to be heard above the others.

As we left the restaurant we saw a station wagon bearing the name of the only daily newspaper in the county parked in front of the police station. A reporter and photographer, locked out like everyone else, were interviewing the people standing along the sidewalk.

"That's only the beginning. Mabel Whatley probably will get a bonus for this," I grunted to my wife."

I couldn't have been a better prophet. Shortly after noon some official looking dudes from Washington camped out in Chief Doyle's office and the next day there were more reporters from around the country in town than there were local residents.

Three television crews had joined the newshawks after the Associated Press picked up the story and spread it over the wires.

The Washington group spent three days checking out the James farm. They finally reported that they had found no evidence to back up Mike's story. A weasel worded press release blamed Chief Doyle for not sealing off the farm before the trampers had flattened every square foot of the field along Cooper Road.

The town was famous for a week. The newsmen and newswomen eventually proclaimed the story a hoax and accused Mike James of making up the story.

The outsiders left town abruptly and it was time for the gang to concentrate on the opening day of the trout season.

On opening day Brad, Skip, Spunky and I arrived at the river long before daylight. We had opted not to fish the infamous creek, but selected a narrow river into which the creek flows about a half mile from the James farm.

Fast Eddie was not with us because he had a teacher's meeting in the morning, but hoped to join us before noon.

We were assembling our fly rods at the meeting point when Spunky shouted: "Be quiet!" and then more softly "I think I hear a whirring noise."

"You better speak softer than that or they are likely to put you in the bed next to Mike's," I cautioned. "People will think you're nuts too."

Then we all heard the noise. It sounded like a giant kitchen mixer. We stood dumbfounded as a green fluorescent thing came wobbling past us 100 feet in the air. As it passed overhead we saw a small figure sitting under a green glass bubble attached to a saucer-like bottom.

Not a word escaped any of our lips as we watched the erratic flight, each lost in his own own thoughts.

The eerie silence was broken by a noise that sounded like two small autos crashing into each other.

"It crashed," Spunky shouted.

"What do we do now?" Skip asked.

Spunky already was at the cab of his truck. He grabbed the pistol he carries in the glove compartment — for safety reasons — and started to run into the swamp.

"Follow me," he said. We all followed.

We had only managed 100 yards when we spotted something green in the trees 75 yards ahead. We slowed our approach to a crawl, each of us looking from side to side, expecting an alien to pounce on us any second.

At 50 yards there was no question it was the thing that had flown over us only minutes before. We could see the pilot trying to escape from the spaceship.

"You stay here," Spunky whispered. No sense in all of us getting killed."

We watched his cautious approach. Suddenly he stood up and motioned for us to follow him. Through the noise of breaking branches I heard Spunky yell:

"It's Fast Eddie."

Fast Eddie's pride was hurt, but not his body. He explained he had been testing his new flying machine and flew over us as a surprise.

"Everything was going good until I clipped the top of that old cedar," he said quietly. "When I spun out of control the lower branches kind of wrapped around me and stopped me from crashing to the ground."

Then in an excited voice he shouted: "Did you see? It flies."

We never said a word, just stood there with our arms crossed in front of our chests.

That seemed to sober him, as if he noticed us for the first time. He said quietly:

"I've got to swear you guys to secrecy. Don't even tell your wives. If this gets out they'll put me in jail. I'll lose my job. I promise I'll chop this thing up and never fly again."

We helped Fast Eddie dismantle his "flying machine," carted it back to our trucks, divvied up the pieces and hid them under tarps in back of two trucks — Spunky's and mine.

We refused to leave until we had opened the trout season.

Fast Eddie using a borrowed rod and some borrowed fluorescent green flies took honors with three brookies. Brad, banned from the pool because he used live bait, limited out in the strangest opening morning any of us ever had.

Because I never reveal a confidence, I've never told anyone that it was Fast Eddie who made our town famous.

Tournament Fever

The gang has never been into tournaments. For us, going fish
ing or hunting is a passion, not a contest. our feeling is that
money is the root of all evil and prizes for the biggest trout, walleye
or deer demeans the reason we fish and hunt.

That's why it was a surprise when Spunky Spriggs suggested we
enter a salmon derby one year when were we fishing Lake Michigan
up near Petoskey. Maybe the fact we had spent most of a windy and
rainy afternoon playing pool at a local pub near our rented cabin
could have had something to do with it.

Of course we played for quarters. Spunky was knocking the pay
balls (the five and nine) in with the weirdest combination shots imag-
inable and picked up nearly $20 before Brad Morrison called it quits.

Spunky and Roger White were the only winners and Spunky suggested he and Roger ante up their winnings to enter the pub's contest
for the biggest salmon caught that weekend. The entry fee was $5
and the winners plunked down the $30 entry fee for themselves, Fast
Eddie Bresler, Skip Fisher, Brad and me.

We set up our own ground rules. Jumping at a bouncing trolling
rod was out and a rotating system of fighting a fish put in place. It
seemed an equitable plan because we were fishing out of two boats
with three anglers in each. We would split the prize money.

Fast Eddie is a nervous sort and, after everyone had hit the sack,
he went out for a stroll on the beach in front of the cabin. The next
day he told me that he had seen some fish jumping in the shallow
water about 150 yards out from the shore.

"I don't know what they were, but it was fun to watch them in the
moonlight," he said. "The weather cleared and I could see them as

well as if the sun was shining."

The weather was clear and fairly calm the next day and we spent the entire day trolling in deep water. The rotation — decided by picking a number (one to three) from Spunky's hat — worked well. No one had a hit.

We visited the pub that night to see if anyone had entered a fish in the contest and had the bartender hoist the biggest salmon caught that day by a local angler. It was a beautiful 25-pounder.

It looked like the winner to me. No one was going to beat that fish before closing time on Sunday night.

"I can beat that," Spunky said. "I've got some special lures in my extra tackle box. That's what I'm going to run tomorrow. I can almost feel the money in my pocket."

The second day was better and the first fish — a 21-pound king — was taken by Roger on a silver and green spoon trolled off a portable downrigger that Brad had mounted on his boat. The rest of us were long lining an assortment of lures and the total number of fish caught was five.

None however was close enough to challenge the fish caught on the first day. We had hoped to fish the next morning and then head home, but even though the high school was closed, Fast Eddie Bresler had an afternoon meeting to attend and we turned in early so that we could get an early start in the morning

About 11 p.m. all hell broke loose. Fast Eddie had turned on the lights and was yelling something about a big fish. We told him to shut up and go back to sleep.

"I caught a big fish" he yelled back. "It's outside."

Five sleepy men struggled out of bed and followed Fast Eddie outside. Sure enough, there on the ground was a big salmon. It was still flopping around.

"How'd you get this one?" Spunky asked.

"I couldn't sleep and thought I'd row out in the little boat the owner told me I could use to see if I could catch a salmon casting. I told Herb this morning that I had seen lots of big fish jumping a couple of hundred yards off shore when I went for a walk last night."

Spunky disappeared while Fast Eddie continued his excited talk. He was back in a flash carrying his scale.

"Let's see what you got," he said, hooking the fish to the scale. "Get dressed, if no one has beaten that 25-pounder, we win the fishing derby."

Ten minutes later Spunky was carrying Fast Eddie's fish into the pub and asking the proprietor to weigh the catch. We stood back while the owner hooked the fish to the scale and let out a low whistle.

"What'd you catch her on?" he asked Fast Eddie.

"I was casting a surface lure," Fast Eddie replied. "I took it out of Herb's box. I don't even know what it's called."

"Well, whatever it's called, the fish weighs 28-plus pounds on my scale and is the winner — that's if no one shows up by midnight. You know, you're the first outsider to ever win a fishing contest in this neck of the woods."

At midnight he handed the $800 purse to Fast Eddie.

"I want to get a picture of this to show the guys, so they don't think I stole Jimbo's money," the owner said.

Two weeks later Fast Eddie stopped by the house after school to show me the new flyrod and reel he had purchased with his share of the purse.

"It's a beauty," I told him.

"I didn't know if I should spend the money, but everyone was so happy about the fish that I didn't tell the truth about how I caught it," he stammered. "But then I thought, what the heck, I did catch it."

"I'll bet you caught it on the FlatFish you took out of my box." I said. "There's nothing illegal about that."

"I didn't catch it on your lure. I caught it with my hands. Remember how I told you fish were jumping all over the lake the night before. I really was casting when that fish jumped about 15 yards from the boat. It dove under surface and jumped a second time, only this time it didn't land in the lake. It landed in the boat. I grabbed it with my hands so it couldn't jump out again."

The Sisters

Everyone in our little town has the greatest respect for Spunky Spriggs. They look up to him.

He is a good husband, father and friend in the eyes of an adoring public. He's also the one everyone in the gang looks up to. He's the best deer hunter whether he's armed with a bow and arrow, shotgun or rifle. As a fixit guy he's the best around. He's a true knight in shining armor.

In other words, he's the man everyone of the gang would like to imitate. His status as the leader of our fishing and hunting gang is unquestioned. That word "unquestioned" almost became questionable because of a certain love affair.

The two ladies entered his life when Spunky was full of life and vigorous to a fault. There was no hill he couldn't climb, no swamp big enough or dense enough to stop his finding areas to hunt where no human may have trod.

The only chink in his armor (at this writing) appeared to surface when he was smitten with Annabelle and her sister, Lulabelle. Because of this love affair he was willing to risk the wrath of his wife and his fellow gang members as well as the worship of adoring townsfolk.

The first time I saw the two sisters was at the town's fireworks display on the fourth of July. Spunky and his wife, Dee, were sitting in their truck which was parked at the county fairgrounds. His wife was trying to ignore the two sisters who were nuzzling her husband and nearly pushing her out of the truck.

Roger White, a gang member in training at the time, was the only one who saw the commotion in the cab of Spunky's truck. He walked over and studied the situation a few seconds before breaking into a fit of laughter.

"Whatcha laughing at?" Spunky hollered over the noise of the fireworks.

"Nothin," Roger said. "And then again it may be something, if those two mutts belong, or belonged, to old man Templeton."

"They were his dogs, but they're mine now."

"That's what I thought when I seen 'em," Roger said. "You know, don't you, that you are the owner of the two most stubborn and stupid beagles this side of hell. They're downright worthless. Whatever you paid for them, you just got fleeced."

"C'mon Roger, Templeton told me the dogs have the best noses and are fast enough to keep any bunnies in sight. They might be a tad too fast for hunting now, but wait until I get through with them. They'll be the best rabbit hounds you've ever hunted over."

Before the day was over Roger had told every member of the gang about Spunky's two dogs. He said he was sure that Spunky couldn't break the dogs from trailing too fast and that Spunky had at last met his match.

The next day I drove out to Spunky's place but he wasn't home. I went around to the back of the barn where I found the two dogs penned up in a corner.

I didn't hear Brad Morrison come up until he said: "I feel sorry for Spunky. Those Templeton hounds may be the dumbest two dogs in the world, but smarter than any man I know, including Spunky."

I drove out to Spunky's place often in the next month, but never found Spunky or the two hounds at home. Dee told me that he took the dogs out every day because he wanted to get them ready for the season — the real rabbit season beginning Dec.1.

"How's he doing?"

"I don't know," Dee said. "I don't think very good because he keeps mumbling about how stubborn they are. He's pretty upset."

"You know they're betting at the Slop Shop that the dogs will break Spunky and that not he, nor anyone else, will ever shoot a rabbit over those dogs. Right now the odds are 2-1 against Spunky and may reach 10-1 before December 1."

Spunky never mentioned the dogs to anyone until the first week of December. When he brought it up a the gang's regular meeting at the Slop Shop, it hit the gang like a bombshell.

"I need five of you guys to go rabbit hunting with me on Saturday morning. I just took a bunch of bets that on Saturday the gang will shoot some cottontails being run by my two hounds from hell.

I got a ton of money riding on this and I need your help."

We agreed and Saturday morning Brad, Skip Fisher, Roger, Fast Eddie Bresler and I were at Spunky's place for a pancake and sausage breakfast. Spunky was cheerful and did the cooking. When we had cleaned up a second serving, Spunky sat down at the table and explained the drill for the morning hunt.

His plan sounded a bit bizarre, but we all agreed to help.

We followed him to a farm about five miles out of town and waited while he chatted with the owner and his wife. He was as sober faced as I've ever seen Spunky.

"Let's go," he said. "I'll take Brad and Roger to their stands and be back to set you other guys up."

When it became my turn, Spunky placed me at the far corner of the farm. He pointed to a pile of rotting logs which had several tunnels leading under them.

"Herb, I'm going to tell you something that I don't want repeated."

"Then don't tell me."

"I got to tell somebody, and you're my best friend. I know you won't betray me. Promise."

"Okay."

"I haven't been able to change those dogs one bit. They've got great noses. In fact their noses are so good they can run a rabbit's trail when they're 25 yards wide of it. The problem is that they are wilder than hell.

"I'll go back and free the dogs to hunt with me. I won't see any rabbits, but I was willing to put up all that dough because I know Lulabelle — she's the fastest — will run any rabbit back to his or her favorite log pile or hole in a heartbeat.

"I've been studying this place for weeks and have pinpointed where they will hole a rabbit. Only this time they will meet their end before they can dive underground or under some heavy obstacle too thick for the dogs. Shoot straight, I'll turn the two hounds from hell loose as soon as I get back to my truck."

Ten minutes later I heard the hounds open up. I was enjoying their good voices when I heard a shot from the direction of the east fence. Seconds later the hounds were silent. A few minutes later the beagle duet started again. A shot was fired from the direction where I thought Fast Eddie was on guard, but the duet continued and was heading straight at me.

A cottontail, running faster than I have ever seen a rabbit run before, was streaking toward my position. I've always shot rabbits running away, but this one was coming straight at me and I could see the dogs 10 yards behind.

I jumped from my hiding place and the rabbit veered to my right. I rolled the bunny over as soon as it was clear of the dogs. The action continued for an hour. I took one more rabbit and counted 11 other shots on the property.

Spunky picked me up last. When I got to the truck, the dogs were in their kennel and 10 rabbits were lined up next to the truck.

"The jerks who dared betting with me are going to sing another tune," Spunky said.

An out-of-state rabbit hunter, who was eating lunch at the Slop Shop, saw and heard everything said when Spunky picked up his winnings. He did everything but cry before Spunky reluctantly sold him Annabelle and Lulabelle and the kennel in the truck for a ridiculously high price

Townspeople weren't sure how Spunky won, but that didn't matter. His reputation grew — after all, he took a city slicker.

Hap Holiday

The date was August 2. I'm sure of the date because I looked at the date on the calendar on the side of the refrigerator. It has a slide bar with a whatchacallit attached that puts a big circle around the day's date.

There was nothing special about the date, but when the better half said Hap Holiday was pulling his ancient truck into the drive, I automatically checked the date.

"You be nice to Hap," my wife said with a glare. "Don't treat him like the village idiot, the way most folks around here do. He can't help it because he's slow."

"I mean, you know, different from other folks," she added.

"Hey Hap," I greeted him as he stepped out of his truck. "Long time, no see. How about a cup of coffee?"

He didn't say anything right off, but after maybe 30 seconds he nodded his head in the affirmative. Hap doesn't talk much.

Come to think of it, it was the first time he had ever come to the house. I wondered if it had anything to do with the boating incident he'd created on July 4.

I could see he was struggling for words and I asked if there was anything I could help him with.

"I was wondering if ... I mean if you have the time ... I know you're a busy man ... maybe I shouldn't have come."

"If I can help, I will," I assured him. "What do you need help with?"

He slowly began to relax and said: "I need somebody to teach me how to back up a trailer. I suppose you heard how I messed up the launch at Phillips Lake?"

I kept a straight face while I told him that I'd heard about his fishtailing his boat and trailer across the access road and blocking it off.

"For an hour I blocked the road. I wished I could disappear. I wanted to crawl under my barn and never come out."

"It couldn't have been that bad, Hap."

"I can never remember which way I'm supposed to turn the steering wheel to make the trailer go the way I want it to. My kids want to go fishing, but I can't get up the nerve to try it again and I hoped you'd teach me. My wife told me I should ask."

"I'll help all I can. I've got my trailer behind the barn. Why don't I hitch it to the back of your truck and give you a lesson."

"No," he said. "I don't want to mess up your fishin' stuff. I'll go home and get my boat and trailer. I don't have to back it up to get it out of the yard."

When I walked back into the kitchen my wife started to laugh and gave me that you got to be kidding look.

"This should be good," she started. "You teaching anyone to back up a boat trailer is hilarious. I remember you fuming and cussing that summer when we went fishing at that small lake in the northern part of the county and you scraped paint off both sides of the boat on the trees along both sides of the road.

"I still remember the fisherman who drove up after us. He watched for 10 minutes before almost yanking you out the truck and backing your boat trailer down to the access ramp. Remember what he said."

"No, I don't remember."

"He said I hope you don't mind, but I only got a week's vacation."

"Well, if you remember so much. Do you remember I had to back the boat up 100 yards on a narrow and twisting path through a pine plantation to get to the lake? In cases like that anything can happen."

"It did," she smirked.

Hap, boat and trailer attached to his truck, turned into the drive a few minutes later and put an end to the what could have become a scene. I met him in the driveway and went over the fundamentals of backing up a trailer.

Our front yard is wide open close to the road and I told him to circle the barn and drive to the clear area.

He was a much quicker learner than I thought he would be. So much so that I suggested we go to Pelt Lake and go through a dress rehearsal before he took the kids out.

I could see him tense up when he saw the water, but talked him through the various maneuvers to get the boat lined up in front of the ramp.

"Now you can back her straight up," I said.

I think I was more nervous than he was as he inched the trailer into the water until the stern of the boat was floating.

"That's all there is to it," I said. "I'd bet that in a week or so people will be calling you the expert."

Hap broke into a broad grin. The gaps between his teeth showed when he shouted: "Yeeeah! I'm going to look at it from the outside," he shouted and jumped from the truck He bumped the gear's lever in the process.

Instantly I felt a slight movement. The truck started to roll an inch or two at a time. I tried to slide over to the drivers side, but my jeans became skewered on an errant spring sticking up through the passenger's seat.

"Hap, I can't reach the emergency brake," I yelled. "Jump in and set the brake before the truck rolls into the lake!"

The next thing I know Hap is slithering through the passenger side window and trying to scramble over me and get to the emergency brake. I saw water gurgling up through the floorboard.

My life passed before my eyes because I knew I was going to drown. I was trapped in a sinking truck by a treacherous coiled spring.

Hap's yell snapped me back to reality.

"Whoopee, I done it. I got the boat in the water by myself — without anybody helping me. Ain't that the greatest?"

Two hours later — after a tow truck had pulled Hap's truck out of the water which was midway up the doors and another hour after someone had retrieved the derelict boat that had broken loose of the trailer and drifted across the lake — I walked into my kitchen and was greeted by my better half.

"Where you been? And don't go looking for dinner. I fed it to the dog."

Benched

The definition of the word "couth," according to The New World Dictionary, is refined, polished, civilized, etc. It also notes the opposite of refined, polished and civilized is uncouth.

I'll bet this is the first time you've ever seen either word in an outdoor publication. Probably the last time, too, although some form of the word may appear in the ensuing paragraphs.

The gang during its existence, which dates back to Catholic high school, has never been accused of being uncouth, except maybe the time Spunky Spriggs bit the calf of a defensive lineman during a game for the area's football championship.

The good Sisters would have been appalled if they knew what Spunky had done, but I'm sure they would have displayed the silver trophy at the school's front doors in any event.

The question of the gang's couth didn't stem from Spunky particularly, but on four members, Spunky, Brad Morrison, Skip Fisher and myself. It arose from an innocent event during the hunting season in our senior year.

The four of us were in a good mood when Skip's dad offered us the use of his hunting cabin for the last weekend of the deer season, He called it a championship weekend for the team's best players.

The best players' tag may have been true for Spunky, but the rest of us were bit players. Oh, we were big enough, but football demands more than size, even in our neck of the woods.

I suppose by high school football standards we were big for the era with Spunky the biggest at 220 pounds. Most of our opponents topped around 160. I admit to 210 pounds at the time, Skip weighed about 200 and Brad, a butterball center at 205 rounded out the big four.

We ate dinner at home before leaving for the Fisher cabin and refueled with a loaf of bread and a jar of peanut butter before turning in for the night.. We were up two hours before daylight, packed a lunch and polished off several stacks of pancakes before Skip led us to the stands recommended by his dad.

We hunted all day. Twenty five deer crossed in front of our blinds, but all were does. Shooting does was not legal back then.

We played pinochle until almost midnight and had only one argument. The argument (Brad's argument) was not about cards, but whether we should go to Mass the next morning before we went hunting.

"I figured we wouldn't go at all," Spunky said. "Now deal."

Brad was quite put out and mumbled something about all of us being sorry about the decision.

"Hey, no one's going to firebomb the cabin. So shut up about it."

There was no bomb or fire the next morning. Skip was the first to leave the cabin and go to the privy. He wasn't gone long."

"Wow, it's cold," he shouted. "I checked the thermometer and it's 15 below. I think I'm going back to bed."

None of us went back to bed. We were all in our blinds an hour before sun up. It was so frosty that we could hear the deer moving around us after daylight, but a ground fog caused by the cold air against the warmer ground made it hard to see them.

It was eerie. I heard deer running at me on a trail 25 yards from my stand. I saw blurred images of all 15 of them jumping a fence and disappearing in the grayness.

"Let's get out of here, it's too spooky for me," Spunky shouted.

Brad and Skip already had the fireplace roaring when we arrived at the cabin.

"Well what do we do now," Skip asked.

"Let's play cards, we don't have to go until this afternoon," Skip said. "I...."

"I wanted everyone's suggestions," Spunky interrupted. "Brad, what do you say?"

"I say we eat breakfast, pack the car and go home. We can stop at St. James Church in Whitehall on the way home."

Well that's exactly what we did. After a dozen scrambled eggs, a loaf and a half of bread, a jar of strawberry jam and a half pound of thick bacon we walked up the short steps to the 100 year-year-old church.

Mass had already started and an usher beckoned us to the second row center pew. We tried to stay at the back, but the young priest interrupted his prayers to invite us to follow the usher's directions.

I thought for a minute that I recognized a silhouette in back near the left wall, but embarrassed by all attention, it didn't register. We got to the pew and the people slid over leaving just enough room for the four of us.

We all sat down at the same time. There was a loud CRACK and the four of us were sitting on the floor in the midst of a bunch of odd looking bits of wood that once had been the pew.

After the laughter subsided the ushers led us to a side wall where we stood for the rest of the service.

We laughed about it all of the way home and before first class on Monday.

I had hardly settled in my chair when I was told to go to Mother Esmeralda's office. (Principals are called Mother instead of Sister). I was surprised to see Spunky, Brad and Skip in her office when I got there.

"I called you four to the office for two reasons: One, I hope one of you got a deer and the Sisters can count on some venison this week and two — because I wanted you to know that I was at St. James Church yesterday for Mass.

"When that pew crashed I didn't know whether to laugh or cry. I decided to laugh with the rest of the congregation.

"Now I have a special assignment for each of you. Look up the word "COUTH" and tell me later if you have any.

"The reason I ask is that one of the ushers told me after Mass that the trouble with youngsters these days is that they don't have any couth."

Launch

I believe in signs. They don't have to be printed signs or spoken signs. An icy stare will do.

Signs sometimes surface at the oddest times — like the morning after Brad Morrison and I had returned from a nine-day trip to the Upper Peninsula.

It was a grueling trip. We spent the mornings and evenings trolling and drifting for walleyes in Little Bay de Noc, chasing brown trout on the Escanaba River, trolling for pike on Millecoquins and South Manistique lakes, fishing and watching terns dive into Brevoort Lake for supper, eating out every night and hopping from one motel to another.

It was typical of the hard life an outdoor writer leads in search of new places to fish, new ideas and new methods of fishing. I needed a rest that Saturday, the first day of a holiday weekend.

Fishing and new fishing methods were the last things on my mind because all signs pointed to finish painting the house. At first I demurred, but after an icy stare, I reluctantly agreed to finish painting the house.

It's not like I shirk my household duties because I had painted three sides of the house over the previous three years — at the rate of one side a year.

I was dragging the ladder out of the garage as Spunky Spriggs was driving by. He slammed on the brakes and pulled into the driveway.

"Whatcha doing?"

"I'm going to finish painting the house. Why?"

"Would you and Mary like to join us at Skip's place this afternoon for a barbecue?"

Spunky knew there was nothing I liked better than barbecued ribs cooked over a charcoal fire 200 feet away from a public launch site. City folks may not think watching boats get launched and unlaunched is a lot of fun, but we rural folks get our kicks where we can.

The thought of watching the activity at a boat launch brought a smile, but I made signs that it wouldn't be a good idea to drop the painting. Spunky never was much of a sign reader.

"I'll ask Mary if she'd like to go."

A few minutes later Spunky walked out and told me he'd see me at Skip's.

My wife came out and told me that she told Spunky we'd come.

"A day off might improve your disposition after nine days of hard work," she said. "You can start painting tomorrow."

Two hours later we were sipping a cool beverage sitting in Skip's backyard, a stone's throw from the public access site.

It's a good launch facility on a decent-sized lake. It has three parallel launch ramps and a pair of courtesy docks. The only problem with the site is that a shallow bar runs across the entrance with only a 10-foot wide channel through it.

All sorts of funny things often happen a short distance from the docks.

Skip Fisher asked about the fishing trip and I told him it was a good trip, except for the time I had to take Morrison back to the motel so he could shower and change clothes.

"What! Did Brad fall in the lake again?" he asked.

"Naw, but he got messed up at a boat launch when he tried to be a Good Samaritan."

"Sounds like Brad."

I took a couple of sips of my beverage and popped a few chips into my mouth. I've learned from experience that it's better sometimes to not seem eager to relate a story. If it turns out badly, everyone groans and moans, but if they force you to tell it, they can't complain too much.

I waited until I had everyone's attention before telling them what happened to Brad on South Manistique Lake.

"Two couples were launching a 16-footer, which was way too big for the site. They got the boat in okay, but couldn't back it out because the rear end of the boat was nudged up against a little sand bar.

"The skipper — a guy with the egg salad on the bill of his cap — elevated both motors and jumped into the lake. He sank into soft muck at the base of the dock, but did manage to get the boat turned so the bow was facing the lake. He was steaming and not just from exertion.

Brad was standing on the courtesy pier while all this was going on. I was standing next to my boat 15 feet away.

The skipper tried to inch the boat away from the pier, but because of the low RPMs couldn't get steerage. Brad was trying to push the boat around to get it pointed in the right direction when the skipper suddenly gunned the engines.

A stream of water, sand and who knows what cascaded out from the motors and covered the dock and poor old Brad. Brad's glasses were covered with mud. I had to lead him off the dock. He was so mad he didn't care if I choked to death from laughing.

"I don't think he liked riding back to the motel in the boat either because I wouldn't let him ride in my new truck."

Everyone laughed, but when I got to the part about Brad riding in the back of the truck I also got three icy stares from the wives when I got to the part about locking him out of the truck. I think I would have received more than the icy stares if I had brought the truck home with mud all over the upholstery.

Boat traffic had picked up during my narration and we started paying more attention to the launch site next door until the ribs and chicken were done. Nothing interesting was going on until my wife asked if I knew what the guy at the boat launch was hollering about.

All conversation stopped. A couple obviously were getting ready to launch a pretty 20-footer. The man was standing in the boat and hollering profanities at his wife who was sitting behind the wheel of the truck. A sanitized version follows.

"It's lined up okay, just put it in reverse and give it the juice," he hollered to his wife. "When I tell you to stop, hit the brakes and the boat will slide off the trailer."

While the lady was backing up the guy was hollering "Faster, faster," and when he told her to stop, her braking wasn't crisp enough and the boat didn't slide off the trailer into the water.

The guy began cussing again — louder and more explicitly. He told her to pull farther up the ramp and get up some speed before jamming on the brake. The stern of the boat was 50 yards away from the water when the truck started back a second time.

The woman had the trailer moving pretty good on her second try. By the time the guy told her to stop the back the wheels of the trailer were four feet into the water. The woman really stood on the brakes. Nothing happened, except her husband had to catch himself from falling.

The ensuing tirade made our wives think about retreating to the house. Spunky's wife was so upset she suggested he go over and punch the guy out.

Even from 200 feet we could see that the woman was crying, but the woman pulled the truck almost to the parking lot, stopped briefly, shifted into reverse and roared backward toward the lake. She slammed on the brakes before her husband could call stop.

The car shuddered to a stop, the trailer shuddered to a stop and the boat shuddered to a stop, but the husband didn't. He sailed over the stern and bellyflopped into the lake 10 feet behind the boat.

The woman screamed. The husband let out string of vile words as the six of us began applauding.

The boater, turned swimmer, started in on his wife again and was running to the truck when a big fellow grabbed him by his shirt.

We heard the big guy yell — "Shut Up." He dragged the guy back to the trailer and pointed to the tie downs which the guy had forgotten to untie.

We could see the woman trying to conceal it, but the smile on her face was apparent as she climbed into the passenger side of the truck. The couple left without putting the boat into the water.

The wife's performance seemed to make the barbecued ribs and chicken taste sweeter than ever, and I noticed a particular icy stare had thawed. Yes sir, like I wrote earlier, there's a lot to be said for watching boats get launched and unlaunched.

Ultimate Sacrifice

Years ago there was a radio show called "Can You Top This?" If there was any way to describe the Tuesday meetings of our gang at the Slop Shop it would be that program because we were always trying to top the narrator of the last tale.

Come to think of it, this fetish — any thing or activity to which one is irrationally devoted — is probably what has held the gang together for so many years.

We meet formally once a month at the back table in the only watering hole for miles around. We missed few Tuesdays starting with the month we became of age. That doesn't mean everyone was personally present, because a job downstate for instance, is why one rule grants an automatic "present in spirit but not in person" entry in the unofficial minutes.

Don't get me wrong. We're not a bunch of boozers, but it's the only place in town to meet unless you rent a church hall. We might not be heavy drinkers, but we surely could set any church back a thousand years.

Friends have asked what we have left to talk about because during most weeks of the year we have fished together, hunted together or dropped in for a cup of coffee at each others homes.

They think we are conspiring to corner all the good fishing spots or wiring in on all of the big bucks in the county. Well, to set the record straight, the gang gave me permission to give you a sampling of what happens on "our" Tuesday each month — come rain, snow, tornado or hurricane.

Spunky Spriggs said it may be the last time anyone reads his name because I'll run the risk of losing the confidence of my editors.

"To hell with my editors," I told him. "I'm going to write it anyway."

A narration of a typical Tuesday meet follows.

The meeting started slowly with Fast Eddie Bresler telling some innocuous story about a big catfish his Uncle Leroy caught in Florida the previous weekend. Fast Eddie said he caught it on a "corn bag," a take off on a northern spawn bag.

We laughed politely and Skip Fisher began a story told to him by Billy Rogell, a shortstop for the Detroit Tigers back in the 30's. Skip had met Rogell while he worked in Detroit during World War II.

"Rogell told me he was hunting just over a ridge above a swamp near Atlanta, Mich., when he sees a six-point poking along heavy cover at the edge of the swamp. He waited for the buck to step into a small clearing in the brush and popped him.

"The buck dropped in his tracks and Rogell scrambled down the hill to where the buck lay. He tagged the deer, took off his coat and hung it on the branch he had leaned his rifle against. He was about to field dress the buck when it kicked him in the chest and tottered off on a path along the swamp's edge.

"Rogell said he grabbed his hunting jacket and rifle and started after the buck. The deer was hit hard and Rogell was only about 20 yards behind it when he heard a shot and saw the deer fall.

He said he could hear a hunter scrambling down from the ridge and waited until the hunter had reached the deer before stepping our from behind some cedar branches.

"Nice deer," he told the hunter.

"It's my first rack," the hunter said. "I'm really excited."

"That's my deer," Rogell said he told the hunter and got the argument he expected. The basis of the hunter's argument was filled with a lot of 'I shot it' sentences. Rogell said he let the man rant a while before asking him to check the tag attached to the deer's right ear.

"The man checked the tag and looked at the license Rogell had in his hand. The numbers matched. The poor guy headed up the hill, muttering under his breath. About halfway up to the ridge, he stopped and looked down at Rogell. He shouted that he didn't know how he did it, but if he could run fast enough to metal tag the deer he was entitled to it."

More stories followed, but none which seemed to top Skip's saga on the ridge. We were about to leave when Brad Morrison, who listens to more stories than he tells, said: "I hunted pheasants on a piece of land in Lenawee County a couple of years ago with a guy who had permission to hunt there.

53

"We limited out in about 45 minutes and I asked my friend how long he had been hunting this particular run down farm and he told me about 10 years. He told me he almost stopped five years before, but decided that he was willing to make any sacrifice to hunt the best pheasant land around.

"He told me that he gives the landlord a bottle of good whiskey and a box of cigars every year for the privilege to hunt there. I told him that wasn't much of a sacrifice and he said I didn't know the half of it.

"My friend said the owner lives with his dog in the dirtiest — make that the filthiest house he's ever seen. He said he gives the landowner the whiskey and cigars on the rickety porch because he doesn't want to go into the house.

He told Brad that one pre-season he arrived at the house about 2:30 p.m. the week before the season opener and the old man invited him in for a bowl of beans.

He said he didn't know what to do — go into the house and continue to hunt there or offend the old man and start looking for somewhere else to hunt.

Eventually he went in and sat down at a small table. The old man's dog was laying on the floor a few feet away. My friend said all he wanted to do was eat the beans and run. He said the beans looked okay and he took a spoonful. As he did, the dog let out a muffled snarl. It happened every time he dipped the spoon into the bowl.

"My friend told the man that he didn't think the dog liked him very much, but the old man told him not to worry and that the dog won't bite.

"He's harmless," the old man said. "He just gets a little testy when anyone eats from his bowl."

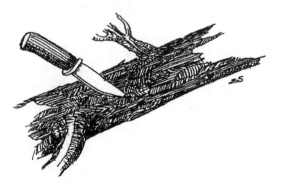

Fast Eddie – The Bird Man

Fast Eddie Bresler wasn't given his Fast Eddie moniker by our gang. He offered that as his sobriquet when I first met him at a New Years Eve party at Spunky Spriggs house years ago.

I don't know who tagged Fast Eddie with his nickname, but whoever it was sure knew the man or the boy, whichever term serves your fancy.

Fast Eddie, who was born in Florida, is the only member of the gang who didn't grow up with the rest of us. The didn't grow up with us factor may be the only thing he has going for him, but he quickly adopted the gang's flair for the obvious. Only in Fast Eddie's case the obvious often becomes the ridiculous.

A science teacher at the local high school, Fast Eddie attaches himself to a dozen projects each year. Things like becoming an expert woodsman, tournament fly caster, professional walleye fisherman, tracker, marksman or ornithologist.

This is a man, who gets lost 50 yards from the deer hunting camp we had used for 10 years, becomes seasick on lakes when the waves reach a foot, loses his way back to the truck while following his footprints in the snow and tries a heart shot and hits the deer in the neck just behind the right ear.

We enjoy his misadventures and all love him for his honesty. None of us would have guessed he aimed for the deer's heart or that he got lost following his own footprints in the snow unless he told us.

All of the above are childs play compared to when Fast Eddie became the birdman. It was a real test of his angelic honesty.

It all started when he announced at one of our regular meetings at the Slop Shop that he was going to get into birds in a big way.

He explained that his sophomore class had asked him some questions about the local bird population and that he was hard pressed to answer many of their questions.

"I felt kind of stupid," he said. "I couldn't answer the simplest questions about the kinds and numbers of birds you Yankees cotton to up here. I decided that I had to learn about northern birds and what I found out could fill a tome."

"What the hecks a tome?" Brad Morrison asked.

"It's a big book," Fast Eddie replied. My mother once told me that I should get some tomes from the library. She said I didn't have to read them. Just carry them around to build up my muscles.

"My mother was a card. You guys would have loved her."

"How are you going to learn about all the local birds?" Spunky asked.

"I got some books from the school library and sent away for A Guide to Field Identification, Birds of North America. It's a good book.

"It defines summer, winter and all year ranges for all birds. It even has a description of the calls that birds make — from a Chickadee to the Heron and the Great Horned Owl.

"I'm learning to call birds to me. I can call a chickadee into my back yard feeder and I've even had a lady Cardinal swoop past me after I imitated the call of the male. I'm going to call in a great Horned Owl.

"I saw one when Ellie Mae and I were taking our evening walk past the woods at the end of our road."

Spunky interrupted: "He's an old one, I wouldn't waste my time trying to fool him."

"I've already got him to answer me," Fast Eddie came back. "It won't take long."

At every meeting of the gang Fast Eddie would regale us with stories of the birds he had seen in the last week. He erected four bird feeders in his yard and birds were all he talked about for months

Spunky eventually put a stop to the bird talk by telling Fast Eddie: "If you haven't got that owl to come into your yard when you call, keep your mouth shut about that danged owl. I've had all the owl poop I can take."

I was worried that Fast Eddie's feelings might be hurt and that he'd drop out of the gang because he looked so downcast.

Three days later Fast Eddie was waiting for me when I returned from an afternoon of fishing. My wife signaled me to talk to her — pronto. I excused myself by telling Fast Eddie I'd get a couple of beers from the fridge.

My wife was waiting for me in the kitchen and motioned for me to come into the hallway leading to the back of the house.

"Don't hurt Fast Eddie, and above all don't laugh at what he's going to tell you," she whispered. "For once in your life don't make any witty remarks. Fast Eddie's your friend and I think he could use some serious advice."

I carried the two brews and sat down next to Fast Eddie on the steps leading from the front porch. He had a faraway look in his eye. We sat in silence for maybe five minutes before he asked: "Why'd Spunky jump on me like that?"

"I don't know, sometimes he gets riled over something that has nothing to do with any of us and goes off like a rocket."

"Funny thing I was ready to tell you guys that I was through trying to call in that owl and the reason for giving up on it."

"Why, you were getting so close," I offered. "It was just a matter of time."

"Not really, Herb. That's what I was going to tell you guys last Tuesday at the Slop Shop. There wasn't any owl. Oh, sure I saw one that night when I was walking with Ellie Mae, but he never answered my hoots."

"Hell, there's got to be an owl. You heard it hoot back at you almost every night."

"No, the father of one of my students told me he had been trying to get an owl to come to his place, but all the owl would do was hoot back."

"So," I said.

"Herb, he lives in the old Spencer house, down the road from my new place. We've been calling to each other night after night for months."

"Uh, Fast Eddie. . . I wouldn't tell that story to anyone, especially the guys in the gang. Let Spunky have the last word."

Black Ice

My wife yelled at me through the kitchen window as I got out of the truck to open the barn door. Her voice had a tinge of urgency to it. I left the truck in the drive and ran to the house.

"Skip's stuck in a ditch somewhere and needs help." she said and handed me the phone.

"Look at all the mud you tracked into the kitchen."

"Skip, what's up?"

"My truck is nose down in a ditch."

""You okay? Where are you?

"I'm okay. I'm at the bar in Potters Grove. Could you drive out and yank my truck free?"

"I'm on the way."

Twenty minutes later I picked up Skip. He told me he was heading for an orchard to pick up a couple of bushels of apples when he hit a patch of black ice.

"Before I could say black ice I was in the ditch. I'm lucky I didn't hit my head on the windshield. It's also a good thing it wasn't a deep ditch or I may have rolled the truck over.

"I did everything right. Took my foot off of the accelerator, trying to slow down without skidding, but on the curve the truck slid off the road. It was like something in slow motion and there wasn't a thing I could do about it."

The black ice had disappeared by the time we pulled up to Skip's truck a few minutes later. Fifteen minutes later Skip's truck was back on the highway.

It was a week later during the gangs last meeting of the year at the Slop Shop that Skip described his misadventure with black ice.

"What's black ice?" Fast Eddie Bresler asked.

Now it's hard enough to describe black ice to a northerner, but trying to describe black ice to someone born and raised in Florida is nearly impossible.

"I don't have the foggiest idea what you all are talking about," Fast Eddie said after listening to each of us try to explain black ice.

After a pause he added, "and I hope I never do."

"See you New Years Eve at my house about seven," he said as the meeting broke up.

The party was well along when Fast Eddie's wife, Ellie Mae said something about black ice to Spunky.

"What do you know about black ice?" Spunky asked.

"Not much, but Fast Eddie said it's tricky ice and that he hopes he never has to drive on it," Ellie Mae answered.

"Fast Eddie must have told you about Skip's experience with black ice."

"When was that?"

"Skip skidded on black ice and ended up in the ditch one afternoon before Christmas and we were trying to explain the phenomenon of black ice to Fast Eddie."

"He never said anything to me about that, only about his accident."

Spunky looked past Ellie Mae at the enclosed porch where the rest of the gang were gathered.

Ellie Mae excused herself to join the women in the living room and Spunky worked his way to the porch.

"Fast Eddie, tell me what you learned about black ice since our last meeting," he asked when Ellie Mae was out of hearing.

Fast Eddie fidgeted on one foot and then the other, his face reddened and he coughed nervously. He looked like a treed raccoon.

"I was going to tell you when the time was right," he stammered.

"The time is right," Spunky said.

I could see the crinkle of a smile radiating from the corners of Spunky's eyes.

"What did Ellie Mae tell you? Hell, it doesn't matter. I may as well fess up. I'm a little ashamed, but you're my friends, right?"

"You got it," Spunky said.

"The Saturday before Christmas I drove into town to buy Ellie Mae a last minute Christmas gift. I was backing into a parking space in front of the discount clothing shop on Front. When I stepped on the brakes nothing happened, except the car sort of skidded a little and I bumped into the front bumper of a red station wagon.

"I didn't think I did any damage, but I didn't want to walk away without telling the owner. So I went into the store, told the cashier what had happened and gave her the license number of the wagon.

"She announced the number and asked, if the owner of the red station wagon was in the store, to please come to the cashiers area. Four big guys came up and the biggest guy told her he was the owner of the station wagon.

"I explained that I had slid into the station wagon. The owner was really ticked. He said he had picked the vehicle up at a Flint dealership earlier that day. All of us walked outside and the owner inspected the station wagon. He said there was no damage and all four of them went back into the store.

"Fifteen minutes later as I was getting into my car the four men came out. I waited until they drove away before getting into my car. I turned right at the next intersection and saw the station wagon stopping for the stop sign at Partridge.

"I was doing 10 miles an hour when I approached the same corner and put on my brakes 60 feet behind the station wagon. I lost control of the car. It was like the car had a mind of its own and I hit the rear bumper of the same station wagon.

"When I got out to see if I did any damage, I slipped and fell on my can. The blacktop didn't look slippery, but it was. I figured it's what you guys call black ice.

"Anyway, when I finally managed to get to my feet, the other guy was checking the rear end of his new vehicle. He towered over me, shook his head and pointed a finger at me. I thought he was going to hit me."

Fast Eddie said that the guy, instead of hitting him, shouted at him.

"Look. I'm going straight through this intersection and I'd appreciate it if you turned right or left. Just don't follow me."

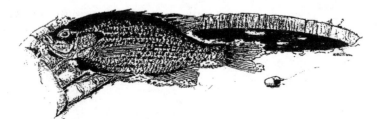

Robin Hood Lives

O f all the years the gang hunted and fished together since grade school graduation I remember being surprised at how hooked we got on hunting with a bow and arrow soon after we read about a bow hunt in one of the three major outdoor magazines back in the 60's.

I called bow hunting retro-revolutionary. That may be coining a new word, but what the heck, if the high-priced writers and masters of the English language can do it, I don't see why an old outdoor writer with a camouflage hat can't take a stab at coining.

We learned about hunting deer with a bow and arrow from a slick outdoor magazine. I can't remember which one because the gang subscribed to the big three — you know which ones I mean — Outdoor Life, Sports Afield and Field & Stream.

Not that we all subscribed to three, but three of us each had one sent to the house and we passed them around like candy.

They were the only slicks available at the time. Nowadays there are so many that postal workers take out hernia insurance because they are lugging some heavy loads to an adoring audience of hunters and fishermen, including fisherwomen and hunteresses. (Theres another coining if I ever saw one.)

We read about archery hunting for several years before actually taking up the sport. We were happy taking our deer with the wide assortment of firearms available at the time. In fact, Brad Morrison, never one noted for his spending, hunted a few years with a shotgun to keep the cost of his sport down.

Spunky Spriggs, living up to his reputation as the gang leader nailed a four-point his first year with a bow. Skip Fisher scored in his second year. They each got a second deer before I managed to bag a spike in my fifth year.

It was about that time that Brad purchased a bow. He walked into the Slop Shop one night for a meeting with a new bow and the remark "I'm sold, if Herb can shoot a deer with a bow, anyone can."

Our wives weren't too happy. Instead of taking care of chores around the house or farm we always were practicing with our bows, comparing arrows or talking about this or that new archery gadget on the market.

We were into bow hunting — really into it — at the time Fast Eddie Bresler became an adopted member of the gang. Being a teacher and all, he had the where-with-all to buy the best archery equipment on the market at the time.

Fast Eddie's a little feller, and try as he might, the best he could pull was 40 pounds. I think he practiced every day, but was lucky at first to hit the side of the barn. The rest of the gang were sympathetic and prescribed exercises and weight lifting in an attempt to add strength to his skinny frame.

He had hunted seven years without taking a buck with a bow. Oh, he had his chances. Sometimes the grunt he involuntarily emitted when he pulled the string back scared the deer and his target got away before he got to full draw. However, most times he watched the arrow fly over the deer's head or ricochet between its legs.

He became a little sullen during the archery season. He hunted with us on weekends, but spent most of his after school hours hunting in the woods behind his house. It was a nice woods and it seems (according to his wife) that he got a shot or two almost every time he hunted.

One afternoon Spunky was helping me fix the pump that supplies all of the water to my house when Fast Eddie came roaring into the driveway.

"I got a buck," he yelled as he ran toward us. "He's a big one. Eleven or 12 points. Ellie Mae's away and I want to get some pictures before I field dress it."

He was as excited as I've ever seen a man and we followed him back to his place. Sure enough there was a huge buck stretched out at the base of a tree 15 yards from his blind.

I lifted the deer's head and had to admit it was a beauty.

"How long ago did you hit him?" Spunky asked.

Fast Eddie looked at his watch and said: "About 25 minutes ago.

I was so excited that I sat on his rump until I calmed down. I could hardly walk at first. Then I headed for Herb's."

"Where did you hit him?"

"He was so close, so I shot at his neck. Dropped like a ton of bricks. Look, I want a picture of me kneeling behind the buck and holding up its head. You know, the kind of shot where the top of the torso of the hunter and guide show over the neck of the trophy."

"Okay," I said. "I've never worked a newfangled camera like this. Show me how it works."

I got the hang of it and sent Fast Eddie back to his trophy.

"Okay, I got it figured out. Don't forget to give me a big grin."

Fast Eddie pushed his cap off his face and knelt down behind the deer.

"Hold his head a little higher, a little high ..."

All hell broke loose. While I was focusing the camera, the deer suddenly jumped to its feet, knocking Fast Eddie against the tree. It was deep into the woods within a heartbeat.

"Did you get the picture?"

"Yeah, I got one."

Spunky's voice was steady. "I think your arrow hit a nerve and paralyzed the deer. I'm sorry, Fast Eddie."

"Hey, that's okay. I hit the deer and Herb has my picture to prove it."

Three days later Fast Eddie called to say he got the picture back from the drugstore.

"Hows it look?"

"It's a great shot of the tree."

Fast Eddie Surprises

L ike beauty, the difference between luck and skill often is in the eye of the beholder.

I'd like to have a fin in the bank for every time I've listened to a sportsman describe the fine art of fly fishing, the nuances of wing shooting or the computer-like skill it takes to down a running trophy buck in heavy cover.

Come to think of it, I may have been guilty of boasting about an amazing feat of skill on occasion during the 50-plus years I've been involved with the outdoors.

You can't say that about Spunky Spriggs. He is the consummate outdoorsman. He handles a fly rod as if it were a magic wand. He shoots a shotgun as well as anyone, as long as there's an object with feathers in front of him. He's taken more moving deer than most men have killed in a lifetime

Spunky wears his outdoor skills on his chest the way a love-sick teenager wears his heart on his sleeve. His skill is so great that it never has been necessary for him to tell a lie – big or small.

The reason I'm sure of that is that he has never deviated from the original version of any outdoor adventure. That's a lot to say about a man who often forgets birthdays, anniversaries and other things a happily married man should remember.

Try as we will, none of the gang has ever been able to trip him up. He's so good, the gang has come to the conclusion he is telling the truth.

The same can't be said for Fast Eddie Bresler. In his case "skill" is spelled "LUCK."

Fast Eddie's first ice fishing trip with Spunky and me could have ended in disaster, what with him being attached to a portable ice shanty that was sliding across the lake faster than the proverbial speeding bullet. He survived the ride and caught most of the fish.

It was that trip which caused Spunky, Brad Morrison, Skip Fisher and me to wait three years before inviting Fast Eddie to join our deer camp.

I've never seen a happier man than when we asked him to go with us. That's when we found out that he had never fired anything larger than a .20-gauge shotgun or at anything bigger than a quail. He admitted that he never once hit any of them.

Spunky set up a firing range at the gravel pit behind his place and we tried to teach him to shoot.

He got so he could hit a piece of cardboard filling the opening in a tire on occasion. However, he couldn't come close to a tire Spunky had rigged to slide down a cable to get him familiar with shooting at a moving target. He was still pretty raw when we ran out of time to teach him anymore.

"Don't shoot at any deer that's moving," I told Fast Eddie when I dropped him off at his stand on opening morning.

"I'm so excited that I don't think I'll be able hit anything standing either," he whispered. "What time is it legal to shoot?"

"Right about daylight. I told him don't go moving around. Remember, if feel you must move, walk straight out to the car and stay on the two-track while walking around. Are you sure you can find the car?'

"I can find it. All I have to do is follow the orange ribbons you tied on the trees," he said.

I walked farther down the ridge to my blind. It was just getting light when movement at the bottom of the little valley caught my attention.

I put the binoculars to my eyes and made out a deer poking along the bottom toward Fast Eddie's blind. It looked like it might be a small spikehorn, but I needed more light to be sure.

I never did make out any horns. A couple of does sauntered along the same run about 70 yards away and disappeared in Fast Eddie's direction.

I was wondering how he was getting along when I heard a shot, then another. And another. A few seconds passed before a fourth shot echoed through the woods . I thought about checking on Fast Eddie right away, but the shots sounded like they came from the road.

About mid-morning I sauntered over to Fast Eddie's blind. He wasn't sitting. He wasn't there and I decided to walk out to the road to see if anything was wrong or he needed any help.

Fast Eddie was standing next to the car, his rifle cradled in his arms.

He rushed over when he saw me as I was making my way through a plot of evergreens. "Did you hear the shooting?" he shouted, his eyes as large as saucers, his eyes as large as saucers.

"Yeah, was that you?"

"No. but I was here when a big buck walked through those oaks over there and stood in that little clearing," he said pointing about 35 yards across the road. "I was talking to this older gentleman when it happened."

"Who shot?"

"The older gentleman. He fired four times at the buck and all it did was stand there. Finally, it ran off that way."

"Did the old man follow its trail? And why didn't you shoot?'

"He looked around at the ground where the deer stood for a few minutes and couldn't find any blood. He went looking for his son.

"Why didn't you shoot?"

"When the old man showed up, I leaned my rifle against a tree. I didn't want to have him think I was some kind of greenhorn.

"What were you doing on the road that early?

"I got cold and I walked out here to get warm."

No one connected on opening day and we were back in the same stands before daylight the next morning. Shortly after it got light enough to see, a four-point came off the ridge across from me and walked to within 20 yards of where I sat huddled in a clump or evergreens. The deer never knew what hit him.

I heard a shot out off the road while I was field dressing the deer, but waited until noon before dragging the buck to the car.

"Wow, you got one," Fast Eddie said. "It's nice."

"Did you hear a shot from out here on the road? It was about 15 minutes after I took my deer and was field dressing it."

"I didn't hear any shots, but I got a shot at that big buck I saw yesterday."

"You shot? What were you doing on the road that early? Get cold again?"

Fast Eddie was jumping around like a cat with a dead mouse.

"No, but I figured that if that buck came through here that early yesterday, he might just come by again about the same time. That's why I walked back to my truck."

"I hardly had time to get behind the truck when he came through the same opening in the trees. And he stopped in the same place as yesterday."

"That buck's leading a charmed life," I said. "Shot at a number of times the past two days and still around."

"No, he's not," Fast Eddie blubbered. "C'mon, he's over here. I don't know what to do next."

Forty yards off the road lay a perfectly formed eight-point. I rolled him over, looking for an entrance wound, but couldn't find one.

"I hit him in the neck, just behind the left ear," Fast Eddie said. "I remember Spunky saying that's where he likes to aim."

Great Depression Relived

They say a depression in a road is no more than an inverted bump. If that's the case, the Great Depression of the 30's was a valley.

The original gang — Spunky Spriggs, Brad Morrison, Skip Fisher and me — lived through the big "D" and maybe are better off for it. Fast Eddie Bresler who is just a kid in comparison to the original gang, never experienced it, and in my opinion, is the worse off for it.

Why does this stuff about the Great Depression (hereafter to be referred to as the "GD" have to do with an outdoor story?

Not much, but our living through it for old times sake, was a delightful experience. It was Spunky's idea. At least we blame him or thank him for it, depending upon our viewpoints at any given time during our reliving of the GD during a fishing week a few years ago.

It all started at the Slop Shop where many of our adventures — or out-of-life experiences — begin. Come to think of it, a lot of crazy stuff starts at the Slop Shop, our favorite meeting place in town. At least my wife thinks so.

Well anyway, Spunky was orating on the subject of modern fishing. His list of items we use today sounded like he had recently received a catalog from an on-line hunting and fishing computerized company.

"You know, we got it easy," Spunky began. "We have GPS to locate fishing hotspots, a graph to locate fish under the water and an outboard motor to get us to the hotspot within minutes. Even if it is on the other side of the lake or two miles up or down the river.

"We have fish finders to give us a good idea of the size of the fish we are going to catch, and a radio with a continuing weather update so we don't get caught in a storm. We have lures in a trillion colors and shapes and we even have green nightcrawlers if we happen to be fishing for bass."

He stopped to catch his breath and waited for some kind of response.

"You aren't just talking without something in mind," Brad spoke up. "What's your point?"

"My point is that I think we ought to fish one week without all the gadgets we have acquired over the years. I think we ought to let Fast Eddie experience the GD, if only for a week. Let him discover how hard it was catching enough fish to eat during a week's vacation or why there weren't many limit catches back then."

We hashed it over during the evening and Eileen O'Conner, the waitress, got involved and said she'd like to come along and find out how we'd act when we got skunked. That statement solidified the Spunky's idea to do it, but without Eileen.

Two nights before we were to leave for a week of fishing we met at Spunky's place to offer for inspection the things we were going to take. Spunky acted like a Marine Sergeant as he inspected the items — throwing several of my offerings out because they were too new.

It wasn't so bad because most of us are pack rats and have old fishing equipment squirreled away in our basements, barns and garages. The day before the inspection I remember telling my wife that the gang finally found out why we've been saving this junk.

"Why's that?" she asked.

"So we can make damn fools of ourselves trying to catch fish while everyone around us will be filling their coolers.

"Aw, you guys are good fishermen, you'll fill your coolers in no time."

"We can't take coolers. None of us had a cooler during the GD. We hung our fish on ropes over the side of the boat. I'm surprised Spunky is letting us take our boats, but he's offered to kill anyone who tries to start a motor."

"Why would he do that?"

"Because none of us had a motor during the GD and we are trying to go back to our fishing roots. We all have to row our boats to wherever we want to fish."

"Poor dears," she mimicked a whine.

My fishing tackle consisted of two five-foot steel casting rods and reels, some old 15-pound black braided fishing line, one of the world's first FlatFish, a red and white Bass-O-Reno, two trolleys (for shore fishing), an assortment of hooks, sinkers (new one's allowed), a medium sized wooden box filled with nightcrawlers and wet newspapers, a bunch of corks from wine bottles and two flashlights.

Everyone was similarly equipped except Fast Eddie who was armed with two cane poles (compliments of Brad and Skip).

On the first day no one did very well. Spunky managed a couple of bass and Fast Eddie amassed a dozen bluegills. The fish went into the cottage's refrigerator because we couldn't find anything that would do as an ice box.

By the third day, however, both boats began catching lots of bluegills because we adapted to conditions. Actually we talked to other guests at the resort and they told us they were catching fish on grasshoppers.

Spunky objected to using grasshoppers until I told him my dad and I frequently used them. I caught them in hedgerows bordering our cornfields and stuffed them into a glass jar that had an air hole punched in the lid.

My hands looked like they'd been splattered by someone chewing Mail Pouch — just like they did when I was a kid.

We kept the outboards silent all week. Folks at the resort thought we were nuts to row a boat when there was an outboard hooked to the stern, but we stuck it out all week. They were dumbfounded when they heard that we had not used the shower all week, but cleaned up in the lake.

The local weekly got wind of us (make that got wind of what we were doing) and came out to take pictures of the weird guys using cane poles and oars.

The GD inverted depression that we called a valley didn't look as deep after the week. We agreed we had a good GD vacation.

Ice Fishing Seminar

A s usual Fast Eddie Bresler started the whole idea of an ice fishing seminar with a question. You'd think a high school science teacher would be more comfortable with answers, not questions.

The question he asked on Saturday morning several years ago was: "What's so difficult about learning how to ice fish?

"If you remember the first time I went ice fishing with Spunky Spriggs and Herb, I caught most of the fish. Imagine a Florida native outfishing a couple of seasoned veterans. My science class got a big charge out of that."

Spunky's dander was up quicker than a dandelion in a freshly planted garden.

"How many fish did you catch the last time we went ice fishing and the 40 times before that?" Spunky asked with a tinge of sarcasm in his voice.

"Besides, when you caught the walleyes, Herb and I dug the hole in the ice, loaned you our best jigs and dressed you from head to toe. How many fish have you caught on your own? Have you won any of our first fish or biggest fish kitties?"

"I didn't mean to rile you, but as I look at it, all you have to do is drill a hole in the ice and you're in business," he said. "At least, that's how it looks to me. Anybody can do that. Right?"

I could tell Spunky was fuming by the way he summoned Eileen O'Conner to the table and ordered a round for the gang. There was a crispness to his voice. Skip Fisher, Brad Morrison and myself recognized his "don't interrupt me demeanor."

He gulped down half a can of suds and looked Fast Eddie in the eye. After several seconds of silence he said: "You got a lot to learn, teacher, and your education is going to begin this weekend. That is, if you don't have papers to correct or some other lame excuse."

"Don't get mad, Spunky. I was just stating something which I feel is obvious," Fast Eddie said with hurt in his voice.

"I don't get mad," Spunky said. "I get even."

He looked at Brad, Skip and me as if he was waiting for one of us to say something. When none of us offered a word, Spunky muttered something about expecting more support from his buddies.

"How cold is it supposed to get tonight?" he asked. "There's been a thin layer of ice on our bluegill lake for a week now. If it gets into the '20s the next three nights I expect we'll be able to fish on it by the weekend.

"We'll take Fast Eddie. He'll use his own lure and bait of choice and he can show us how easy it is to catch fish through the ice. The only stipulation is that he can't fish in any of our holes. Each of us will throw a buck into the pot and the one who catches the most fish takes it all.

"We don't need power augers for first ice so we chop the holes with a spud or crowbar or anything you want to bring for the chopping purpose. That goes for you too, Fast Eddie."

Spunky finished his beer in one swig: "Good night gentlemen," he called over his shoulder as he walked toward the door. He winked at me as he passed my chair.

Fast Eddie was visibly shaken by Spunky's attitude. "I sure put my foot in my mouth again, didn't I ?"

We all assured Fast Eddie that Spunky would get over whatever was bothering him and that everything would be fine on Saturday.

"But you had better be there," I told Fast Eddie as we parted in front of the Slop Shop.

"I really don't want to fish on New Year's Day, but I'll be there. I don't want to lose a friend.

It stayed cold the next three days and after a tame New Year's Eve I picked up Brad and Fast Eddie. We met Spunky and Brad at the local diner and Spunky seemed to be in a very good mood.

"I want to apologize to all of you, especially Fast Eddie," Spunky said. "When I got home from the Slop Shop I told Dee that we couldn't be out too late on New Year's Eve because Fast Eddie had begged me to teach him the nuances of ice fishing.

"I told her I didn't want to disappoint Fast Eddie because she likes him a lot better than I like the Sherman's who had invited us over to celebrate the New Year.

"That's why I put on the mad show in hopes it would get back to Dee. It did and it worked out swell for me."

We all told Spunky he was a jackass and couldn't understand why he didn't let us in on the charade.

"Because one of you would have let the cat out of the bag at home and Dee would have been all over me and I would have had to party with the Shermans until dawn. This way I get to go fishing with the gang and my wife's not ticked off at me."

We were the only customers at the bait store and the only ones at the lake a few minutes later

Spunky immediately began tutoring Fast Eddie about the dangers of walking out on first ice.

"Remember first ice isn't uniform," he cautioned. "There will be solid spots and weak spots. Use your spud to check the ice ahead of you. Let the sharp edge fall on the ice. If it digs into the ice easily, it's not safe to walk on. And stay in shallow water.

"If the ice gives way, you want to be standing on the bottom of the lake and not treading water.

"Fast Eddie you're the lightest of the group, you lead the way."

Fast Eddie, who was relieved that Spunky wasn't mad at him, followed his idol's instructions and we were fishing inside of a weedbed only 20 yards from shore.

The teacher caught the first bluegill of the year. He also caught the second and the third. Spunky started to walk over to Fast Eddie to check the color of the teardrop he was using.

He had taken a half dozen steps when the ice gave way under him. In a heartbeat he was standing in water up to his waist and sputtering something about how sorry Fast Eddie was going would be if he tells his science class about this fishing trip.

Bear Invades Our Town

If memory serves me correctly, the day the bear invaded our little town was about 25 years ago, but they still talk about it in the Slop Shop — especially when tourists are in town.

It's one of those yarns that persist even after the truth is known, but that may be because it originated in the town's favorite watering hole. In fact the Slop Shop is the only watering hole in town.

Sometimes two or three years go by before it's mentioned again. Usually Maude Klautenzimmer brings it up when there are strangers in the saloon. Old Maude is up there in years, nigh onto 100, a couple of old-timers believe. She also has trouble remembering things.

Like the time she came in for a beer dressed in a flimsy night-gown because she forgot to get dressed before leaving the house.

She may forget to get dressed occasionally, but Maude remembers the bear like it was yesterday and believes what she tells any stranger who will listen to her.

"I was sitting at the first table," she always begins, "when all of a sudden a big bear, the biggest I ever saw, came creeping up to the front door. It must have weighed at least 500 pounds.

"They tell me it stopped at the front door, but I was gone by then. I ran all the way home and locked my door and windows for the first time in my life.

"I never knew how they got that bear to leave town, but that Spriggs boy had something to do with it. Saved the town, he did. I think they gave him a medal. We had a lot of bears around town then, but there's not so many any more. The town has grown and too many more people living around town now must have scared them off."

The strangers usually pump Maude for more information, but

her memory kicks out and your guess is as good as mine what she tells them. I do know that her memory has to be jogged every once in a while with a glass of beer.

In the spirit of Paul Harvey, the radio guy, the rest of the story is a bit different. Spunky Spriggs deserved a medal, but he never got one.

On the day the bear came to town, Spunky and I planned to hunt a meandering swamp not too far out of town. It was during the second week of deer season. At first the whole gang, except Fast Eddie Bresler, was going to drive the swamp a little ways out of town, but everyone canceled out because of work, honey-do's or family matters.

We had talked about where we were going to hunt at the gang's last meeting and were surprised to see Fast Eddie drive up in his Volkswagen Beetle just as Spunky and I were going to start a silent drive of the swamp.

"Hey, what are you doing, skipping school today?" I asked. "Teachers aren't supposed to skip school,"

"Boiler broke and they closed school for the rest of the week," he said.

We watched Fast Eddie pull a pair of boots and a shotgun out of the back seat of the Volkswagen.

"Why the shotgun?" Spunky asked. "You do know we are hunting deer and your rifle would be better than that toy."

"I'm using No. 4 buckshot because I supposed any shot I might get will be at a running deer. I want a bigger pattern than a single rifle bullet. See, I'm trying to think about what I'm doing like you guys are always telling me."

Spunky shrugged his shoulders and started off along the edge of a narrow finger of the swamp. "Fast Eddie will come with me and you take the other ridge. Maybe one of us will chase a buck to the other edge of the swamp. Go slow. Deer like to sneak around behind a hunter in this kind of cover. Stop every two or three steps and watch the area ahead of you. And look behind you too, because deer like to circle behind the hunters."

"I know the drill. We've been talking about it all the way out," I said, a little miffed at the reminder.

I was still muttering to myself about a half hour later when I heard the unmistakable sound of a shotgun. Seconds later Spunky's rifle barked and Fast Eddie began screaming frantically.

"Herb, over here," Spunky sounded excited.

I could hear Fast Eddie's scream over Spunky's voice and I scraped chin and shins crashing through the swamp to get there as fast as possible.

I saw them through a screen of brush. Spunky was kneeling next to Fast Eddie and appeared to be holding him down.

"What happened?" I shouted as I broke through the last of the brush into the clearing where Spunky was holding Fast Eddie pinned to the ground.

"A bear — a big bear! He almost got me!" Fast Eddie screamed.

I saw the bear laying on the ground about 15 feet from where Spunky was holding Fast Eddie tight to the ground. It took a full 20 minutes before Fast Eddie was able to stand and then walk over to the dead bear and examine it.

Quietly Spunky asked Fast Eddie if he remembered the little lane that followed the contour of the swamp they had just come through.

"Uh Huh," Fast Eddie replied. "You mean that narrow hiking path?"

"That's the one. It's too wide for my truck but I'd bet your Beetle would fit it like a glove. Get your car. You'll have to back down the lane because there's no place to turn it around in here. Back up until you see the big maple tree.

"You can't miss it. Wait for us there. It's only about 200 yards from here. Herb and I will field dress the bear and somehow carry or drag it to your car. Remember, wait there — no matter how long. We'll bring the bear to you."

"Something bothering you?" I asked after Fast Eddie had walked out of the clearing. "I could have gone for the car."

"Herb, that was close. We were moseying along when Fast Eddies sees this bear. The bear is crossing the lane he was on and Fast Eddie ups and pumps his No. 4's into the bear.I crouched down to get a better look and I catch a glimpse of this critter heading right for him. I yelled "SHOOT" but I can see him ejecting shells without firing a round.

"I had one little opening and I prayed I'd make a good shot. The bear crumpled about 10 yards in front of him and landed almost at his feet. That's why he and I are all shook up.

"I sent Fast Eddie to go for his car to give him something to do. It'll help calm him down."

Spunky field dressed the 300 plus-pound bear while I found a branch strong enough to hold up the bear. We carried the bear on our shoulders and had to stop every 10 or so steps to rest. It took us an hour to carry the bear out to Fast Eddie's Beetle and nearly an hour to position it on the car and 10 minutes to help Fast Eddie worm his way through the window and behind the wheel.

"I'll meet you at the Slop Shop," he said and pulled away.

Now you know the rest of the story.

Faster Than A Speeding Bullet

Fast Eddie Bresler, the last member to be included in the gang, was given the moniker, Fast Eddie, because he is always in a hurry. He has no "waits" in him, but over the years he has done things which almost replaced the Fast in Fast Eddie Bresler.

There was the time he stepped off the bank of a river into water just below his chin or how about the time he built a chartreuse spaceship and scared half the state with his test flights. Who could forget the time he drove his car into a stranger's car twice within 10 minutes. The list could go on and on.

We were talking about that at a meeting at the Slop Shop when Fast Eddie was attending a seminar as part of a teachers continuing education program in the school district.

"Fast Eddie never ceases to amaze me," Brad Morrison said. "Sometimes I dream about him and wake up in a cold sweat without ever finding out if he got out of this or that scrape.

"When that happens, I know I'm going to have a bad night. I start thinking about his track record and start laughing so hard I can't get back to sleep and spend the rest of the night sitting at the kitchen table drinking coffee."

It should be pointed out that the gang never tagged the Fast Eddie to his name. The nickname was coined by friends in Florida when he was a teacher in training. When he moved north to take a job teaching at the local high school he moved into the house next to Spunky Spriggs.

When I met him at a New Year's Eve party at Spunky's house, he came up and introduced himself as Fast Eddie Bresler.

Spunky, Skip Fisher and I sympathized with Brad's sleepless night because Fast Eddie escapades keep coming up at the darndest times. One time I started laughing out loud during my pastor's exhortation about loving thy neighbor."

"What story was that?" asked Roger White, a potential gang member.

"One year Herb made some connections with a farmer in the Thumb," Spunky began. "I think he mentioned the farmer's name in some story and the guy invited him and his friends to hunt pheasants on his place.

"We all were excited about the invitation, especially Fast Eddie since he had never shot a pheasant in his life. As always, he asked a thousand questions about hunting pheasants."

We told him he should do well, what with his being called Fast Eddie and all because the pheasants are very apt to run, and, if you want any pheasants, you'd better chase whichever dog was running the bird.

"I can run," Fast Eddie said and repeated stories about when he was a member of his high school's state champion track team and was picked for All-State honors on the second team.

He had often showed us a picture of himself drinking a chocolate milk shake and holding his second place award.

The first time I saw the picture I asked him why he was holding the milk shake.

"I like shakes," he said.. "I always was drinking a milk shake when I was a teenager. I still drink about three a day when I'm not hanging out with you guys. My favorite color is the color of a milk shake."

Three weeks later Spunky, Brad, Skip, myself and Fast Eddie pulled into Oliver Phillipot's barnyard. The dairy farmer invited us in to meet his wife, Mary Terese, and have a cup of coffee before we began the hut. He told us that his boys had shot a limit of pheasants the first two days of the season, but that there were plenty of birds left for us.

"The boys have made the birds nervous. They're as skittish as hell," Oliver said. "I hope you got your running shoes on because you'll have to keep up with them if you want to get a shot."

Oliver pointed out the areas of land he owned and which neighbors' lands we could hunt. We let Spunky's dog, Sparky, out of his kennel in the back of the truck and started to work a stubble field running adjacent to a big field where Oliver's cows grazed every day.

Within minutes Sparky went on point. As Spunky approached his dog, two hens ran out from under thin cover a few feet from the Brittany's nose and scampered under the fence and raced across the pasture land.

It was a scenario that was repeated often. Fast Eddie crawled under the fence to the pasture to act as a blocker which we hoped would force the birds into the air. The birds responded by running further down the fence line before crossing in front of Fast Eddie.

This, of course forced Fast Eddie to run faster and eventually he did manage to shoot at and miss a rooster which flushed within range.

When we caught up to Fast Eddie he was panting and mumbling something about "these northern birds sure can run."

"We teach our southern birds to be gentlemen and to fly slower. I'll just have to run faster to get them into the air sooner."

Fast Eddie was right because within minutes he ran fast enough to force a bird away from the fence and into the air in front of Spunky who downed the bird at long range.

"I'm getting there," Fast Eddie said. "I seem to keep sliding while trying to pick up enough speed to cut the birds off closer to you guys. Give me a second to catch my wind and we'll have another go at it."

After a 10 minute blow for Fast Eddie to catch his wind, the line of hunters in the stubble began moving forward again.

"Bird running," Brad, who was closest to the fence, called.

I was the farthest from the fence and out of the shooting picture. I was amazed at how fast Fast Eddie could run. I was amazed at how far he went into the air when he seemed to slip on something in the pasture.

The next thing we heard was a string of cuss words (in a soft southern dialect) coming from Fast Eddie as he struggled to get on his feet. Brad was the first to get close to him. It looked like he was about to offer Fast Eddie a hand, but changed his mind.

We all came up to find Fast Eddie trying to clean himself off after tripping on a slick mass of cattle dung. He appeared to be covered from head to foot.

"I swear I don't know what it is, but it looks like a human chocolate shake, " Skip opined.

Tippicanoe and Eddie Too

It was in the 1960's. Two days before New Years day to be exact. The gang, minus Fast Eddie Bresler, was holding a meeting at the Slop Shop in preparation of our annual New Years gathering.

We were telling stories of the past year's fishing and hunting experiences. Fast Eddie's name kept coming up in the conversation. Sort of a reminder of the times Fast Eddie did this or that.

Brad Morrison, never known as a diplomat, suddenly remarked during the conversation with the observation that if it wasn't for Fast Eddie we wouldn't have anything to talk about.

"That's surprising," I said, "after all he's the newest member of the gang. I hope he's having a good time back home in Florida during the Christmas break."

"I hope there's someone around to pull him out of whatever he's fallen into this time," Spunky said. "He can be a big pain in the you know what, but I'd miss the little feller if he wasn't around. You guys are getting to be a bunch of old fuddy-duddies. You're not much fun any more."

"Is that a call to disband the gang?" I asked.

"No, I'm just as big or bigger fuddy-duddy than any of you. It's just that we're getting too cautious and have to study our next step forever before moving on."

Skip Fisher, usually the taciturn one, suggested we think about something really bizarre that Fast Eddie did during the year. "Maybe it'll pull us out of this funk we're in," he said.

Suggestions immediately were placed on the table and the mood of the gang changed quicker than Spunky can get his scope sighted on a running deer. We all were trying to grab the attention with a Fast Eddie story.

"Whoa," Spunky silenced the gang. "I promised to be home early so that I could help start cookin' and bakin' the hors d'oeuvres for tomorrow night's party. Start mentioning Fast Eddie capers and when we have the best one we can talk that one to death."

After a few minutes we decided that the spring canoe/trout trip in the Upper Peninsula would help us remember Fast Eddie better than any other hunting and fishing experience during the past 12 months.

So many years and rivers have passed in the last 30 to 40 years that none of us could remember (from the warmth and comfort of our table at the Slop Shop) the name of the river we had decided to canoe and fish shortly after the season opener.

It may have been the Ontonagon or the Iron or the Escanaba, but it makes little difference for purposes of our recollections of Fast Eddie.

We had parked one truck at the take-out point and motored some five or six miles upstream in the second truck to the point we were going to begin fishing. Fast Eddie and Spunky were in one canoe and Brad Morrison and I in another. I'd rather have fished with Spunky, but Fast Eddie wasn't too swift in a canoe.

Spunky told us later how they had fished a few nice pools and caught and released several smaller fish. Our goal was to keep enough for a shore meal which we were to eat at a location Spunky would pick out after they had caught their lunch.

About mid-morning they got into some nice browns and a half hour later had enough fish for lunch, including several for Brad and me.

We hadn't caught enough trout for lunch — at least for two some-thing-bigger-than-slim — active canoeists, but we did have enough for a taste. Twice our problem was that when we came to a good-looking pool we were having control trouble and canoed right through it.

We spent most of our fishing time on the bank whenever we could find a place with a tiny bit of casting space. We almost overshot the spot where Spunky and Fast Eddie had built a fire and started the shore lunch.

As we laboriously made our way to them we noticed that Fast Eddie was clothed in the blanket which had covered the small basket containing miscellaneous plastic dishes, salt, rolls, etc.

Spunky steadied the canoe while we alighted. From the care he took to get us ashore without getting wet, I had assumed that he hadn't been that careful when Fast Eddie disembarked.

"How'd Fast Eddie get wet?" I asked Spunky.

"Ask him."

You could see Fast Eddie was uncomfortable when I asked him how it happened. His face was beet red and he stammered a little as he started.

"We caught the fish for lunch a short ways up the river and Spunky backed the canoe into this spot when he saw there was enough room for the four of us, a fire and place to store the canoes.

"When we reached the bank, Spunky got out of the canoe and started to lift it onto the bank. The water was shallow — not up to Spunky's knees — so I hopped out. It was then that I heard him yell 'stay seated'.

"By that time I was up to my shoulders and still looking for something to stand on. When I came up I grabbed Spunky's hand and he pulled me to shore.

"I didn't know that the shelf that Spunky was standing on was only three feet wide. It was seven feet deep where I jumped out of the canoe."

The Early Days

I saw SpunkySpriggs wheel his bike into the driveway, put it into high gear and skid to a stop at the back porch.

"What's up," I asked.

"My grandpa said I could come along on the Thanksgiving Day hunt . . . and that I could bring one friend. Wanna go?"

I was 10 years old at the time and there was nothing better I wanted to do on Thanksgiving. The thought of it made me weak. I started to half run to the back door to ask mom, but my hand stopped short of the doorknob.

"Suppose she won't let me go."

"Grandpa said he will call her if it'll help."

"No, I better do this myself."

A plan already had formed in my mind and I went in to face the music. Mom, as expected, erupted when I asked her if I could go.

"I got enough problems running this place since your dad passed. I don't need another one."

I stood up to her like a man — I lied.

"I guess I got to tell Spunky he can't go hunting."

"You mean you can't go," came the quick reply.

"No, I mean Spunky, cuz his grandpa said he couldn't go unless he brought his best friend. He'll be disappointed."

I walked out to the back porch and told Spunky what my mother had said. "Let's walk out toward the barn and you pick up some stones and throw them into the field. Make like your mad and don't look back at the house."

"Why?"

"Maybe it'll make her change her mind."

We had just turned the corner. That gave me just enough time to tell Spunky what I told when I heard her calling me. We slowly and soberly walked up to the porch.

"Herb tells me your grandpa has invited you to hunt with him on Thanksgiving if I let Herb go along" Mom said when we got to the porch. I thought your family had filled all its deer licenses."

Spunky told her that all the grownups had shot a deer and that they were going to hunt rabbits over at Weller's swamp on Thanksgiving. "I'd sure like to go, but if Herb can't go, neither can I," he said.

You could see the brain cells working in Mom's eyes.

"I don't know. I'll have to think some more about it. What are you going to hunt with? Your Grandfather isn't going to let you carry a shotgun is he?"

"No, maam, we're going to carry our BB guns," Spunky answered.

"I'll let you know after school tomorrow," Mom said.

"I hope you can come," Spunky said as he hopped on his bike and headed home.

School day lasted forever. Twice Sister Esmeralda had me stand in the corner because I was wool gathering, as she put it. Spunky got off the school bus at my stop and the two of us went into the house. Mom was beginning to fix supper.

"Kin I go hunting tomorrow?" Spunky asked her.

"Can I go hunting tomorrow?" she asked in her best Sister Esmeralda sound alike.

"You want to come too?"

"No I don't want to go hunting tomorrow, Spunky. I was correcting your English. Now ask me your question again."

"Can I go hunting tomorrow?"

"Well since you will be using BB guns I guess you can't hurt yourself or someone else too bad, I think it will be okay."

The shouts of joy about floored Mom and we raced outside and rolled in the leaves because we were so happy.

"I told you it would work," were my parting words to Spunky.

I had been on the porch 15 minutes before Spunky and his grandpa turned into the driveway. I threw my BB gun into the truck bed and climbed in.

It didn't take long to get to Weller's place. Spunky's two uncles were waiting for us. Mrs. Weller invited us in for pancakes. I remember like it was yesterday that she put a cup of coffee and a plate with the world's largest pancake in front of me.

"Sam made the syrup last year. I sorry we don't have any milk in the house so you younguns is got to drink coffee. That okay?"

I thought it was a great day — my first hunt and my first cup of coffee.

While the uncles were getting the hounds out of their cages, Spunky's grandpa handed Spunky and me a single shot 20 gauge shotgun.

Before we started grandpa explained to Spunky and me the finer points of hunter safety."

"Spunky, you hunt alongside of me, and Herb, you go with Uncle Floyd. And be careful you don't shoot someone or yourselves. I can't afford to let you get hurt, after all you're supposed to be hunting with BB guns."

At that point I realized Mom must have called him. I thought Spunky's grandpa was the greatest guy alive. No one got hurt, but the hunt caused me a great deal of inner anguish until I was older.

The reason — I shot my first rabbit on that hunt and wasn't able to tell anyone about it.

Getting Lost Is Easy — Getting Unlost Is Something Else

S punky Spriggs told Fast Eddie: "Remember that getting lost is easy, It's getting unlost that's the hard part." We were standing on a fire lane in our local federal forest when Spunky spoke the advice to Fast Eddie one morning about a month before the gang's morel mushroom picking excursions. The section in front of us was our prime hunting grounds.

We were there because the gang, especially Brad Morrison, was getting tired of traipsing all over the area looking for a lost Fast Eddie. Spunky and I took it upon ourselves to tutor Fast Eddie in the things you have to pay attention to so that you "don't get lost."

"It's all a matter of observing things — buildings, man made things and the characteristics of the land," Spunky told Fast Eddie as soon as we got out of the truck. "Now what do you see that will remind you of where we parked the truck."

"All I see is that the truck is parked on a sharp left to right curve," Fast Eddie answered.

"What else?"

There was a few minutes delay before Fast Eddie pointed to a stand of birch trees 50 yards ahead of the truck.

"That's good, but what else?"

We stood there a good five minutes before I told Fast Eddie to look beyond where we were going to walk. "Way beyond and all around," was the way I put it.

Exasperated I finally told Fast Eddie to look at the skyline.

"I'm sorry. I don't see anything but that signal tower maybe a mile across the road from where we are going."

"Score one," Spunky said. "You'll be able to see that tower a long time before you see the birches or the sharp bend in the road. Your points of reference are no good because this lane has a lot of sharp turns and there are birch clumps all over the area.

"But, you'll be able to see that tower for miles. First check your compass to make sure you know the direction we're heading. Okay. Let's go and point out to us the things you see that will be able to lead you back to the truck."

Every time Fast Eddie pointed out what he thought was a vital signpost, Spunky asked him to look for the tower. He had trouble finding it until Spunky told him to check his compass and look in the direction where we came from.

"Hey, that's great," Fast Eddie said. "I'm not going to get lost this year."

We spent five hours in the woods with Fast Eddie and he was able to find the tower most times. Occasionally he'd forget to check his compass to get a general reading of where the tower should be, but he appeared to have absorbed most of our instructions.

Two weeks later the gang met at the Slop Shop to settle final preparations for the first morel foray of the season. Spunky and I had found some early morels while on a scouting mission during the week. The upcoming weekend looked like a good time to start hunting in earnest.

"We may be a bit early, but we've had some rain and with the warm sun over the last two days, we may hit it right," Spunky said

Spunky is our morel guru. I suspect he can smell the darned things. I've seen him walk 25 yards to a morel growing on the side of a ditch. We met the next Saturday so Fast Eddie, who was still teaching school, could join us. We parked in the exact spot as the day when we oriented Fast Eddie to the terrain.

Spunky and I wanted Fast Eddie to go with us, but he wanted to hunt with Roger White (the second best morel hunter) because he wanted to pick Roger's brain for information on how to fix a balky lawn mower. We agreed to meet back at the truck for lunch.

There weren't as many morels as we thought and most of the gang were back at the truck early. The only one missing was Fast Eddie.

"Where's Fast Eddie?" Spunky asked Roger as he emerged from the woods.

"Beat's me," Roger said." He stuck to me like glue until I finished explaining what he had to do to his riding mower. I moseyed in the direction he was heading and called his name off and on for five minutes, but he never answered me.

"Let's eat," I said. "Fast Eddie's probably walking toward that tower and will be here in a few minutes."

"Don't count on it," Brad offered. "I almost laughed when you two said you were going to straighten out his sense of direction. I bet he has trouble finding the bathroom in his own house."

We were well into our rest session when Spunky said he forgot that he had to get something from a little store we passed on the way into the lane

"I'll be back in a jiff," he said

While Spunky was gone we told "Lost Stories." The star, or goat, of each story was Fast Eddie. We laughed, but we knew that when Spunky got back we would have a tough afternoon looking for him.

We started to stir into upright position when we heard Spunky's truck bouncing along the rutted fire lane.

"Look's like someone with him," Skip Fisher said. "I wonder who he ran into."

Spunky was out of the truck almost before it stopped rolling. Fast Eddie was a little slow in getting out.

"Where'd you find him?" Roger asked.

"On the main highway, he was about 100 yards down in the valley heading for a radio tower. I figured that's where'd the absent minded professor would be. He saw the tower, forgot to check his compass and was walking to it when I drove up."

Spunky looked at me and shrugged his shoulders.

"Hey, look at it this way," I said. "You done good and we don't have to hike around all afternoon looking for him."

Matches and Bears

The conversation about the difference between Michigan's two peninsulas started about halfway across the Mackinac Bridge. We talked mostly about the different terrain and lifestyles of citizens living in the Upper and Lower peninsulas. Eventually we got onto the subjects of bear populations of the two land masses.

Fast Eddie Bresler said he didn't like bears too much since he helped carry a live bear out of a swamp along the AuSable River and nearly got killed by another while deer hunting.

"They're mean," he said. "If I never see another bear in the woods, it will be too soon. Let's change the subject."

We rode in silence for about 10 minutes or so before Spunky Spriggs told Fast Eddie he should have stayed home because he was liable to see a bear at any time along some of the trout stream his friend had chosen to fish.

"You never told me there were a lot of bears up here," Fast Eddie said. "I'm not afraid of bears. Remember I'm the only guy in this truck who's handled a live bear. I plain out don't like bears."

"Yep, most bears in Michigan live in the Upper Peninsula," Spunky responded. "Why, I remember the time ..."

"Knock off the bear talk. I don't want to listen."

Spunky nodded his head and the conversation for the remainder of the trip was about stream fishing for brookies.

We arrived in Ontonagon well after dark and Spunky introduced his friend, Jay Rhea, who had invited us up for a few days of fishing.

"I promise you the best trout fishing you've ever seen," Jay said. "I'm going to take you into some streams that haven't seen a fisherman in years because downstaters are afraid to go too far from paved roads or creature comforts."

After an hour of trout talk we went to bed. Jay told us to sleep in because the trout we'd be after fed all day.

"That's why they're so fat," Jay said.

Carmen, Jay's wife, had coffee and steaming plates of flapjacks ready for us when we emerged from the bedroom about 8 a.m. Jay showed us some pictures he had taken on the stream we were going to fish that day.

"You never mentioned the name of the stream," I remarked.

"Don't intend to either, especially with a writer along because I don't want the whole world to know about it," Jay answered. "Say any of you guys smoke besides the writer?"

"Nope."

"Then I better give you non-smokers some matches. I'm sure the pipe smoker's got his own."

Fifteen minutes later Jay swung his four passenger truck off the county road onto a two-track. A mile or two later he turned into a grown-over burn area. If you looked hard enough, you could tell that maybe a vehicle had been through this way a year or two before.

Twice he had to stop the truck and check to make sure he was still on the "road." Eventually we started into a forest area. After 20 minutes of bouncing off rock, trees and through shallow ditches we came to a swamp blocking his way.

Jay had brought us to the edge of a swamp where two creeks joined to form a bigger stream which made a sharp turn back into the cedars. We scrambled out of the truck, or I should say we grunted our way out, especially those in the shallow seating area behind the front seat.

"Okay, here's what we're going to do," Jay started.

He looked and sounded like a Marine Drill Sergeant I was assigned to in boot camp on Parris Island back in the 40's.

"Here's some matches for the non-smokers and I'll give each of you two strings of firecrackers."

"What's the firecrackers for? It ain't the 4th of July," Spunky said.

"Them's for bears," Jay shot back.

"Bears!" came a chorus from the trio in front of him.

"There are a lot of bears in this area," Jay said. "If one of them critters comes around, light a string of firecrackers. The noise will send them running all the way to the Keeweaw Peninsula. Remember, keep your matches dry. And keep an eye on the weather. It's not good to get caught in a swamp during a lightning or wind storm."

I watched Jay and Spunky disappear in the swamp before I started for the creek on the right. Fast Eddie was still standing in the semi-clearing.

"You going to be okay?" I called.

"Yeah, sure. Why?"

I was worried about Fast Eddie and turned around to watch him for a few minutes before working upstream. He was floating a spinner into the current, letting the spinner down just above a tangle of roots and stumps on the stream bottom.

I was about to start fishing when a gust of wind and a clap of thunder changed my mind. I looked around at Fast Eddie. He was still in the middle of the stream and his head looked like it was on a swivel. He looked at one side and then the other until he had covered 360 degrees.

He started to wade back to where the truck was parked and got almost to the bank when he stumbled in the fast current and fell backward into the stream.

He disappeared from sight briefly, but eventually regained his footing and surfaced, spitting out tannic-stained water.

A tree crashed to the ground somewhere in the swamp. Fast Eddie was still in the middle of the stream and grabbing at his shirt pocket.

I thought he was having a heart attack until I saw a string of firecrackers and the book of matches. He stood there frantically trying to light the soggy matches.

Suddenly he turned and waded upstream until he got abreast of the truck. He got out of the stream and ran to the truck. He didn't try the doors. Instead he scrambled onto the hood and then the top of the truck's cab.

His head snapped this way and that at every noise in the swamp and there was plenty of that — trees rubbing together in the wind, limbs snapping and rotted trees crashing to the ground.

I wanted to help him, but his strange antics held me riveted in place until I heard Jay and Spunky hurrying toward me.

It had started to rain while the three of us watched Fast Eddie from the edge of the swamp.

"Let's go save the poor beggar before he has a heart attack," I said.

"No, wait," Jay said and touched a match to a string of firecrackers.

Fast Eddie almost jumped out of his skin.

I never saw anyone so happy to see a human faces as I did when the three of us walked up to the truck.

Before any of us could ask Fast Eddie anything, he shouted:

"I was worried about you guys. When I heard the trees falling I climbed up on the truck to be able to hear better if any of you called for help.

"I'm glad you guys are okay."

Brad Morrison's Prophecy

It's a tradition that our gang gathers around the campfire on the last night of the deer season. It's a time for all of us to let our hair down, a time to let it all hang out and get whatever is on our chests out into the open.

Usually one member after another gets maudlin about what our association with each other means to him.

We were expecting the same this year when Brad Morrison got up to speak. Brad always has been the thinker in the group and when he started we expected more of the same.

We sometimes forget that Brad is a design engineer and his mind is full of computerese (if there is such a word) and what his fellow design engineers might be able to deliver to the world's population in years to come.

"I'm going to make a different speech this year," he started. "I've been thinking about what we all have lived through and what folks can look forward to in the new millennium.

"This century spawned two world wars and a few others which could be counted as near world wars. Our age put us into the second of those two wars. After studying the new sophisticated weaponry and technology in place now, I think we have seen the last of such wars. Gentlemen, we fought in the last World War.

"From now on wars will be fought by pushing buttons and pulling knobs which will wipe out entire populations — men, women and children in a single catastrophic instant."

He paused to refill his glass, looked around to make sure everyone was awake.

"Aside from the wars and population problems of the new millennium, the new millennium is going to have a real effect on us, what we do and how we do it," he continued.

"To keep it simple, let's confine our thoughts to what we have experienced in our hunting and fishing lives in the last century.

" In our personal outdoor lives we have gone from fishing with a cane pole to using precisely engineered reels and graphite rods so slender they resemble a toothpick in diameter.

"We all yanked fish from the water when I began fishing. Now we engage in a 10-minute struggle with a fish half the size of the ones we easily hoisted out of the water with muscle power.

"Fishing has become fun during our lifetime when you take the time think about it. And don't forget we have modern means of transportation and can fly off to Montana or Alaska when the fishing gets too tame for us in Michigan.

"Part of the fun, I suppose is that fisheries experts have been able to grow and plant fish species which were killed off during the last century by pollution and are no longer present in the state's waters. We've had the best of all worlds in the last half of the century.

"I remember Herb and me biking 22 miles when we were kids to catch a few bluegills to put dinner on the table during the Great Depression. We've lived through tough and turbulent times and maybe deserve the advancement in fishing tackle and firearms.

"We've graduated from the long and recurve bows to bows with wheels and pulleys and God knows what else so that we can pull 70 pounds and hold it with our little pinkie until a spot of light shines on the spot we want our arrow to hit. Sitting Bull never had it so good, but he managed.

"The new millennium is here, and who knows, all we may have to do is push a button to release an arrow or kill a deer with a ray of light.

"Fast Eddie (Bresler) is a science teacher. He knows that things unknown and revolutionary probably will be implanted in some genius' head and he, or she, will revolutionize the hunting and fishing industries.

"But we won't have improved compound bows and fishing rods and reels. There will come a day when a hunter will not have to leave his or her easy chair to bag a deer or some exotic animal."

"C'mon, Brad," Spunky interrupted. "You don't mean some scientist is going to develop techniques to program deer to stand outside the back door and wait to be shot?"

"No, but he will develop a little black box that he'll mount on a tree. You won't have to climb into a treestand, but swig your brew at home and look at a monitor. Oh, you'll have to look at the monitor when it starts beeping.

"Then all you will have to do is decide if you want to shoot the animal in the sights of the monitor. If it's a good buck you can push a button and the deer is dead; if it's not good enough for your tastes, you can push a bypass button and the deer lives."

"BULL," came the cry from the gang. "That's impossible."

"What do you think, Fast Eddie?" Brad asked.

"It's impossible now," the science teacher responded.

"See, Brad doesn't know what he's talking about," the rest of the gang shouted in unison.

"But it's entirely possible in the future," Fast Eddie shouted over our noise "God only knows what the future holds."

Brad waved for attention before continuing.

"I want us all to swear an oath tonight," he began. "An irrevocable oath to the effect that none of us will live until Y3K and not have to become indoor-outdoor hunters."

The gang stood and joined hands and repeated after Brad the following: "We solemnly swear . . . that we will do all in our power . . . to depart this land of fish and game before the year 3000 . . . or before scientists or outdoor hucksters . . . have taken away our right to hunt and fish . . . in the traditions of such as Isaac Walton or John Wayne . . . so help me God."

To Give and To Receive

A taxidermist I'm not.
In fact, the only thing I've stuffed (except my face) is a mallard, and that's so long ago that I can't remember the year.

It is safe to say it was the sorriest work of taxidermy art ever, and even today I'm almost ashamed to admit I did it.

Of course my wife has a lot to do with my shame. It all started one morning over breakfast when my wife asked me why the gang was always badgering Fast Eddie.

"Ellie Mae came over yesterday morning while you were out chasing brook trout or something with your gang," my wife began. "She was almost in tears and kept asking why everyone picks on her husband all the time and don't they know that he has feelings too."

"I tried to calm her down and find out what this was all about. She told me it was about the trip for brown trout you guys took a couple of months ago. She told me Fast Eddie hasn't been the same since and that all he does is mope around the house saying that he can't do this to Herb."

I quickly assured my wife that he'd get over it and that the gang didn't mean anything by what we did and that we love Fast Eddie like a brother.

Suddenly I remembered a gate that needed realigning. I muttered something about fixing it and started for the door.

"Not so fast," she said as my hand was on the doorknob. "Sit down and tell me how you tortured Fast Eddie this time."

I knew I was trapped and returned to the table.

"Torture's a little strong," I began. "It's hard not to react when Fast Eddie does something bizarre or unusual."

"Quit weaseling," she interrupted.

"Okay, but you are going to smile when I tell you what it was all about."

My wife got up from the table and poured herself a second cup of coffee. That was most unusual, but she explained it by accusing me of dictating a novel whenever I say I'm going to start at the beginning.

"Well you know we heard about the big trout being taken over on Lake Huron and decided to drive over and check out the reports," I explained.

"The whole gang went over on a Friday evening. We stayed at Otto's place. You remember, Otto Zinger— he went through the fifth grade with all of us except Fast Eddie. Spunky (Spriggs) has kept in touch with him all these years. Otto invited us to stay at his place.

"He doesn't fish, but he told us that he had heard lots of reports about limit catches of browns. Otto told us some of his friends caught them fishing large minnows under slip bobbers on Lake Huron.

"At the time it was a novel way for us to fish for browns, but Otto's report was too good to pass up.

"We fished at a pier near his place and we took up a sizable stretch of the pier's wall. Each of us had two lines in the water. I took the kitty for first fish — a nice five-pounder. An hour later we had six browns on our stringers.

"Fast Eddie hadn't caught a fish. In fact he hadn't had a bite. I think he was more interested in watching scores of ducks diving for minnows."

My wife raised her hand and almost shouted: "No novels, please."

I told her that she asked for the story and that I was trying as well as I could to set the stage so that she would understand why I don't think Ellie Mae's story should upset her so much.

"Well," I continued, "Brad (Morrison) checked Fast Eddie's rig and discovered he was fishing too deep and that his minnow was hiding in the weeds along the bottom and the fish wouldn't see it.

"On Fast Eddie's next cast his bobber had hardly settled upright in the lake when it began bouncing like crazy on the water. Spunky and Brad coached Fast Eddie on when to set the hook. When he reared back to set the hook, his rod bent almost double and line peeled off at full throttle.

"We all thought he had the granddaddy of all browns on until his line lifted out of the water and attempted to fly to the Charity Island.

We all shouted for him to cut the line before he takes it all, but Fast Eddie wouldn't because he wanted to save his 75-cent slip bobber.

"By golly, he eventually brought the ticked off merganser to the pier. Skip (Fisher) climbed down a ladder on the dock, grabbed the bobber and cut Fast Eddie's line. We could see about 10 feet of monofilament line trailing from the merganser's bill as it flew away.

We congratulated him on a great catch and went back to fishing. Ten minutes hadn't passed before Fast Eddie yelled: "Fish On." This time it wasn't a merganser and it was not a trout. It was a cormorant — a bigger and tougher bird than a merganser.

Fast Eddie had it on for five minutes before it broke the line and flew away, taking Fast Eddie's bobber with him.

"We started in on Fast Eddie and began calling him the bird man and teased him about what kind of fowl did he plan to catch next." "An hour later people walking on the pier asked me if I was the duck catcher. I pointed to Fast Eddie and the next thing I know he was the hit of the pier.

"It's the reason why there were more than a dozen people standing around Fast Eddie the next morning when he hooked into a loon. The big bird sort of walked across the water on its wing tips until it broke the line.

"We caught our fill of brown trout in the two days we fished, as you know, and Fast Eddie managed to connect successfully on three fish. On the ride back I suggested to Spunky that three ducks — my apologies to the loon — seemed to merit some sort of award.

"I suggested we present Fast Eddie with my mallard mount at our next meeting at the Slop Shop.

"Of course, after the meeting all of the customers and help present at the Slop Shop got into razzing him and have been quacking every time Fast Eddie walks in the door."

My wife looked me in the eye and started to laugh.

"That's not all of what Ellie Mae came for," my wife said in between giggles. "Ellie Mae really came here to ask if Fast Eddie could return your mallard mounting because Fast Eddie's afraid giving it back might hurt your artistic feelings."

All For One and One For All

It was about three days after the gang returned from a fishing
trip that Brad Morrison phoned to tell me that he had called a
special meeting at the Slop Shop.

"My wife's all over me about how unprepared for emergencies
we are when we go on a trip," he said. "You know Mabel. If I don't
take some action, or look like I'm taking some action, the next month
is going to be you know what around my house."

I sensed he was a bit upset and attempted to calm him down, but
he interrupted."

"I'll tell you all about it when we meet at nine tonight," he said
and hung up the phone.

I mentioned it at the supper table and my wife immediately wanted
to know what happened during our five-day fishing trip that caused
Mabel to be so upset.

"Beats me," I said. "The only thing out of the ordinary was that
Fast Eddie got a hook caught in his skin a couple of times, but we
managed to take care of it in nothing flat."

My wife suddenly got the look of a hound on a scent and kept
boring in for more details. You know, asking the same question in
different ways to see if I changed any facts the second and third time
around.

I remember I made some remark about how excited Mabel gets
sometimes and immediately wished that I had kept my mouth shut.
My wife's defense of the excitable Mabel was so excellent that I
thought she might secretly be taking some law classes while I'm
busy fishing and hunting.

All I know is that I was happy when the time came for me to

leave for the Slop Shop and find out what the problem really was.

I was 15 minutes early, but Brad was already there, drumming his fingers on the red and white oil cloth.

"Hi," I said as I slipped into the chair next to him. "What's this all about?"

"Let's wait until everybody is here," he said.

Skip Fisher and Spunky Spriggs came in together and Fast Eddie Bresler wasn't too far behind.

"How's the finger?" I asked.

Someone else asked the same question at the same time and the words — "How's the" — were in perfect harmony. The last words from the second voice added the word "cheek."

"Fine and fine," Fast Eddie said in answer to the two questions.

Brad interrupted any further discussion with Fast Eddie.

"Let's get to the heart of the reason I asked for the meeting," he said. "I apologize for telling Mabel about Fast Eddie's getting a hook stuck in his right thumb and under his left eye."

"You should apologize," Spunky said. "You know as well as I do that Rule No.1 is — what they don't know, won't hurt em."

"I know the rule, but I wasn't thinking. I still laugh every time I think about how Herb got that hook out of his thumb. And after laughing, I want to spit.

"The reason I called for the meeting was that Mabel wants one of us to take some first aid lessons so that we could handle any emergency that comes up in a professional manner."

"Good idea," Spunky interrupted. "Mabel's your wife. You take the lessons and we'll all feel a whole lot safer.

"Let's order another round."

An hour later when Eileen O'Conner brought the last round to the table she asked a question. "I'm curious about what you guys have been laughing so hard about all evening — if it's not dirty."

"No, it's not dirty," I began. "Last weekend we were at a lake near Alpena and Fast Eddie thought he saw an eagle along the shoreline of the lake and pointed at it the exact second Spunky was casting a Hot-N-Tot at a cluster or rocks along a drop off just off the shoreline.

"Fast Eddie's hand intercepted the lure and one point of the treble hook buried itself in the fat part of his right thumb. A second later I heard the first Southern Style bloody murder scream of my life.

"It lasted only a few seconds, but it was so shrill that made what little hair Skip Morrison has left on his head stand on end.

"When Fast Eddie asked if we could take him to a doctor, I explained how simple it was to shove the hook entirely through the skin, cut off the barb and pull the hook out.

"Fast Eddie said okay, but every time Spunky touched the lure the little fella let out another murderous scream. I knew I had to help and pulled a package of chewing tobacco out of my tackle box, grabbed a big wad and told Fast Eddie to hold it in his mouth for a few minutes to deaden the pain.

"After telling me his body had never touched tobacco, he reluctantly agreed. Within seconds he was leaning over the side of the boat and spitting tobacco leaves all over the lake.

"I grabbed his hand, Spunky pushed the barb through and snapped off the barb with his cutters and pulled the rest of the hook out of Fast Eddie's hand. The operation lasted 10 seconds top. The spitting lasted 10 minutes.

"An hour later Fast Eddie was yanking his lure — not a Hot-N-Tot, but a Rapala — out of some weeds when it flew out of the water and caught itself in his cheek just below his left eye.

"The little fellow didn't say a word or blink an eye for a minute or two. Finally he reached his hand out, asked for another chew and for someone to hold him stationary while Dr. Spriggs was operating."

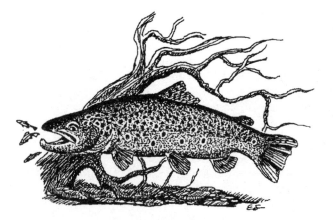

Heads or Tails
The Bear Facts

S ome guys are born under a dark cloud. Fast Eddie Bresler is
one of them. Fortunately, he isn't aware of the curse which
seems to follow him everywhere.

Over the years since he moved to Michigan from the south to
take a job as a science teacher at the area high school he's been in
one scrape after another.

He's so sure to get into some sort of corner that Spunky Spriggs
and I usually invite him along on our outings for laughs whenever
we have something planned. That's why he blames us for many of
his misfortunes. He can, however, get into trouble all by himself.

It's never his fault. As an example, he blames Spunky for the
bear incident and Spunky was 300 miles away helping a relative build
an extension on his house.

Fast Eddie, who at the time was renting the house next to Spunky's
small farm, couldn't resist finding out what The General wanted when
he pulled into Spunky's driveway towing a trailer that looked like a
portable jail cell.

The General, that's what everyone called him, was the area's expert bear authority. He didn't shoot bears and never tasted bear meat.
He trapped them.

According to local lore, The General boasted about trapping every bear that was being held in captivity in the state. The bears were
in zoos, caged at roadside attractions and displayed as part of a couple
of traveling carnivals touring Michigan at the time. Fast Eddie arrived at Spunky's house just in time to hear The General tell Spunky's
wife, Dee, he probably would have to free the bear that he had trapped
along the AuSable River because he didn't have enough help to get

the bear out of the swamp and into his trailer.

"You need help?" Fast Eddie asked.

"Yup, but you're a little puny for this job," The General said after giving Fast Eddie the once over.

"Hey, I can help. I'm a lot stronger than you think."

The General stroked his unkempt beard and studied Fast Eddie's offer for several minutes, a smile playing at the corner of his mouth.

"Okay, we'll try it. There's usually four or five of us, but if I can get Pete to help us, I'll be back to pick you up in a half hour."

While Fast Eddie was waiting, he called me to say that he was going to help The General bring in a bear and asked if I wanted to go along."

I told him not to go, but in the midst of my plea, Fast Eddie cut in and said: "I have to go, he's here."

The General drove his truck and temporary cage to the edge of a high hill overlooking the AuSable River where a quarter of a mile of swamp sprawled between the bottom of the hill and the river.

The General led the way down a steep path which traversed the hill, a mixture of sand and sparse ground cover. It was a hot July afternoon. The General, Fast Eddie and a huge local, named Pete, were soaked with perspiration when they got to the bottom of the hill and began working there way to the river.

"Fast Eddie, over here," The General called.

A minute later Fast Eddie was looking into the eyes of "the biggest" bear he had ever seen.

"The bear, they told me weighed about 300 pounds, was in a trap that he didn't want to be in," Fast Eddie said later that day. "The General was cussing, the bear was snarling and all I could think about was getting out of there."

Fifteen minutes later, The General and Pete had the bear trussed up. Fast Eddie said he kept his distance, staring at the bear, and wondering how they were going to get the bear to the truck at the top of the hill.

Pete sprawled on the ground while The General chopped down a small cedar and began shortening it with his ax.

"What's that for?" Fast Eddie asked.

"A carry pole. We'll tie the critter to the pole and carry it up the hill to the trailer."

Fast Eddie gulped. He studied the bear and decided there was no way he was going to carry the heavy end of the bear, and when it came time to move the bear he decided he was going to be on the lighter end of the bruin – where its head was.

"I'll set the track," The General said. "Lead on Fast Eddie."

Fast Eddie balked. "I'm not going first — I don't know much about climbing hills."

"Okay, get in back," The General ordered.

"No, I want to stay by the head. I'm the smallest and it's lightest by the head."

"If you want to carry the head, it's okay by me, but the head's got to go up the hill first."

"I'll watch," Fast Eddie said and sat down.

The General and Pete argued for several minutes, but finally agreed to let Fast Eddie carry the lighter end and bring up the rear on the way up the hill. There was a hint of mischief in The General's eyes when he said: "Okay, let's go."

"It wasn't too bad at the bottom of the hill," Fast Eddie told me that night. "The pole, about four inches in diameter. was heavy and digging into my shoulder

"I thought The General would give us a rest occasionally, but all he did was walk out behind. I can understand why they call him. The General.

"The big trouble began when we started to climb the hill. At first all that happened was that the bear swayed toward the back of the pole, but its head was a long ways from me.

"As the grade became steeper, the lean of the bear became more pronounced. In fact, it looked like the whole bear, which was thrashing and growling, was slipping down to my end of the pole.

"In desperation I heaved up on the pole and dropped a few inches closer to the end of the pole so that I could get closer to the end. He didn't look like he wanted to stay on the pole."

"I yelled for The General to help, but he seemed to have fallen way behind. Pete was virtually a deaf mute at the other end of the pole. I heaved up on the pole and dropped back a few more inches until I was almost at the end of the pole. It helped, but only for a few minutes.

"The bear was relentless in his slide to my end of the pole. By the time we got to the top of the hill, the bear's head was less than a foot from my midsection. Once on the top and walking to The General's truck I began walking forward while the bear was stationary and hopping back when it started to move its head. If I was a dentist I could have examined its teeth.

"The General reappeared at the top of the hill as if by magic. Pete and I set the bear down and I watched the two of them maneuver the bear into the cage on the trailer."

Fast Eddie said he didn't say a word to The General on the ride back, not even when he offered him two dollars for his help.

Treed By A Trout

It's a wonder the gang has stayed together as long as it has. There are enough irritating incidents which you think would split us asunder.

You know the kinds of irritants that annoy you. Someone gets lost, another leaves some of his fishing gear on the back porch and we waste an hour going back and picking it up and sometimes one or another of us is out of sorts and not very much fun to be with.

Despite it all, we overlook each others faults and plan the next outing before we arrive home. We never mention whatever it was again, although most us think about whatever it was from time to time and hint at it during subsequent trips to get a rise out of whoever was the goat.

There are two incidents involving Skip Fisher that come to mind whenever we are planning a trout fishing expedition. His experiences are the reason we opt to fish creeks and small rivers instead of big, deep and strong flowing streams.

The fact that the two incidents happened to Skip is amazing because he is one of the gang's most conservative and safety conscious members.

The first event occurred before I permanently moved back home after semi-retiring from newspaper work. The event left Skip a changed man.

Skip, Brad Morrison, Spunky Spriggs, Roger White and myself were fishing a stretch of the AuSable River when it happened. The area between Mio and Glennie contains some stretches of big and fast moving water. Skip fished it with two rods — a fly rod and a spinning rod.

Skip's theory was, that if he couldn't reach a fish with his fly rod, he would give it a try with a spinning rod rigged with a clear plastic bubble to allow him to cast a fly rod-sized FlatFish and reach those spots.

None of the gang had much money at the time for top of the line waders or expensive tackle. We made do with what we could afford.

Skip was fishing in tennis shoes over light plastic waders. The waders frequently stuck to his clothing or skin like glue. He constantly had to pay attention because if the waders filled with air they could cause a bubble of air to form under his armpits and literally lift him off the bottom of the stream.

On the day of Skip's first incident, the trio started fishing after they agreed to meet for lunch at one of the stream's familiar landmarks. Spunky, Brad, Roger and I arrived at the appointed time, waited 45 minutes while we ate our lunch before deciding to check on Skip.

We found him 20 minutes later standing in the river and casting leisurely between glances at the shore line.

"Hey, you're late for lunch," Spunky called from the bank 50 yards from where Skip was standing.

Skip's reply was to wave furiously for us to come to him.

When we got nearer to him, Skip started shouting that he was stranded on a rock and needed help to get off.

"Back off upstream," Spunky called from the bank.

"I can't," he shouted back. "The water's over my head. I'm lucky I managed to get a foothold on this rock. I was picked up by an air bubble and felt the rock. I'm lucky I managed to keep my footing. I've been standing here waiting for you guys to help me get off this dog gone rock for almost two hours."

Spunky, who is much taller than Skip waded out toward the rock, but couldn't get to within 25 feet of him.

"Got any ideas" Spunky asked.

"Yeah, I've had a lot of time to think. Cut down a small tree, the thinner the better and swing it out to me. I'll grab it and let the current sweep me into shallower water."

"Brad, there's a hatchet in my truck," Spunky said quietly. "Fetch it for me. Roger and I will take off our waders and stay here in case Skip loses his grip on the rock and starts to float downstream.

"It took Brad 30 minutes to cut down a small poplar and get back to us. Skip's suggestion worked like a charm. When Skip reached lower water he and the watchdogs were able to wade to shore.

"It was hard holding onto that rock with my feet," Skip said and plopped exhausted on the bank of the river. "I've got to rest awhile before I can start walking back to the truck."

A half hour later Skip got to his feet and we started back for the truck. The three of us in the lead hadn't gone too many steps before we realized that Skip wasn't walking with us. We retraced our steps and watched Skip ripping his waders to shreds.

To this day no one, including Skip, can figure out why he hadn't put a belt around his chest to prevent an air bubble from forming. After that experience Skip refused to join us on trout fishing trips to big waters, but he wasn't against helping us eat some of our catch.

Skip's second encounter with death, as he likes to call it, occurred on a small river, or large creek, if you prefer. It changed him more than the first time he thought he was going to drown. We were fishing a stretch of Dynamo Creek that meanders through several swamps and pasture land not far from where we live. We ignored fishing the creek where it passed through farm land and the shallow places along the Dynamo.

Before going much further into the story, I must tell you that Skip is a gentle giant of a man. It's not because he is exceptionally tall, but his girth would rival the famous Friar Tuck featured in the Tales of Robin Hood. He always has been sensitive about his weight and never has told any of us how much he actually weighs.

On this occasion he also failed to show up for lunch and Spunky, Roger and I once again set off to find him. We walked about a quarter of a mile when we heard a faint cry for help. It sounded as if it came from a long way off..

"I wonder what he's gotten himself into this time," Spunky said to no one in particular.

We cut across a marshy peninsula where the creek makes a big bend and were heading upstream when we heard Skip call again. The voice was behind us. We slogged through wet and spongy marsh which made up most of the peninsula on our way to the voice.

We called every few minutes to get a good line on where to find him. It was rough going, but eventually we found him — at least his rear end — draped over a heavy branch of an old cedar growing at the edge of the Dynamo.

It took us several more minutes to reach him because we kept sinking deeper into the quagmire. When we saw him totally we saw that he was holding himself up by his armpits. His feet, ankles and knees were buried in black muck on the creek's bottom.

"Watch out," he rasped. "There's no bottom to this stuff."

"Hey, stay calm, we'll get you out," Spunky said. "Brad you're the lightest, see if you can get far enough out to lift Skip's boots out of the muck."

Spunky held Brad's hand in case he started to sink, but it wasn't necessary. Brad pulled first one boot and the other out of the wet muck. It took some time for Skip to get feeling back into his arms and legs before we half carried and half dragged him to firmer ground

"I was trying to drop a fly on a nice brookie that I saw feeding upstream from me, but with all the brush and overhanging branches of that cedar I couldn't get to him," Skip explained. "I wasn't paying much attention to anything but the trout and stepped into that muck hole.

"It was like being on an elevator and the cable broke. If that tree branch hadn't been there and I hadn't grabbed it, I'd be gone. You never would have found me. How come Brad didn't sink?"

Always the diplomat, Spunky answered: "Cuz he weighs about half as much as you do."

The two incidents changed Skip's life. He still won't fish big water, but he continues to chase trout. Oh, he's a little lighter today — about 125 pounds lighter.

Fast Eddie and The Wolf

Some members get out of sync during the winter. Brad Morrison, for one, began finding excuses for staying home instead of hunting bunnies and snowshoe hares or fishing one of the frozen lakes in our area.

Brad isn't too tall and balked at a snowshoe hunt in the Fletcher Swamp. Spunky Spriggs and I were trying to convince him to join us one weekend a few years ago (well maybe more than a few years ago).

Brad isn't too tall and offered that as an excuse for not hunting with us.

"For you big guys it's okay, but I refuse to go hunting when the snow is deeper than I am tall." he said. "You may have forgotten the time when I stepped into that snow-filled hole someone had used for a fire pit.

"It took me 15 minutes to climb out of the hole and my new deer hunting outfit looked like the inside of a chimney when I did manage to crawl out. No sir, count me out."

We were leaning on him when Fast Eddie Bresler appeared at our table at the Slop Shop just as Brad finished his oratory.

"Hi, you going hunting Saturday?"

Spunky told Fast Eddie that maybe we were and maybe we weren't. "All depends if we can round up a few more guys. Two guys trying to cover even a small patch of the Fletcher Swamp is like trying to stop a leak in a dike with your thumb."

"I'll go with you, if it'll help."

"We could still use another. How about it Brad? Fast Eddie isn't much taller than you and weighs about half of what you weigh."

"I may be able to get the high school principal, Mr. Fowler, to go along. He's always asking about my hunting and fishing excursions and laughing."

Fast Eddie called Spunky the next morning and said "Sour Puss" Fowler would be happy to join us." Spunky told him that we would meet them at Old Man Fletcher's abandoned farmhouse across from the swamp at 8 a.m.

The principal told us the morning of the hunt that he was honored to be invited because Mr. Bresler had told him so much about us and about the fun he had hunting and fishing with the gang.

Spunky led his dogs, Bruce and Buster, across the gravel road and we followed an old trail into the swamps. It was tough walking until we got into the swamp. The cedars and pines were laden with snow and there was a lot less snow on the ground if you stayed under the trees.

"It's like walking through a tunnel," Fast Eddie opined just as Buster opened up on the first game of the day.

From the way Buster ran, we knew he was fast on a snowshoe's trail. Spunky took charge and sent Fowler and Fast Eddie down a lane to our right. For Fowler's benefit he told them to look for the snowshoe long before the dogs get close to them.

"They get way out in front of the dogs and can slip by you if you're not alert," Spunky told them before the two of us headed to the left.

"The hare sounds like he'll be circling in their direction, but keep your eyes open because sometimes hound music will get other hares moving," he said as he hustled further along an old trail.

Ten minutes later I heard the faint baying of the hounds heading toward Fowler and Fast Eddie. I shifted into a position to watch the area between us and caught a glimpse of a snowshoe heading right at me and rolled it over as it attempted to cross 30 yards away.

I hadn't got to the downed hare before I heard two shots from Fast Eddie's direction. A snowshoe suddenly appeared coming from that direction and I bowled it over too. I heard Spunky fire three more times over the next two hours. He showed up 10 minutes later carrying three hares.

"Let's find Fast Eddie and the principal and get out of here," he said. "Some snow fell down my collar and I'm cold."

We hung the hares in a tree and went to get the others. We found the principal and called for Fast Eddie. He didn't answer.

He should be easy to find. We sent the principal back to the trucks and followed Fast Eddie's boot prints in the snow. Three minutes later the footprints led under a big cedar. It looked like a tent with its heavy snow covered branches hanging to the ground. We circled the tree, but could find no exit prints.

Spunky crawled under the tree, cussing every time snow cascaded from the branches into his open shirt.

"Herb, come here," he called. "Something's wrong."

When I got to Spunky's side, he pointed up the tree. Fast Eddie appeared to be stuck in the tree, his body draped over a branch. He was sound asleep. Spunky called his name and he stirred."

"What you doing up there?"

"I'm stuck."

"Why in hell did you climb the tree?"

"I saw a wolf," his voice sounded panicky.

"There's no wolves around here," Spunky said in the softest voice I've ever heard him use. "But if there was, why didn't you shoot it if it threatened you."

"It's illegal."

It took five minutes and a ton of snow falling inside the collars of our coats and down our backs before we were able to get him down out of the tree.

"Don't say anything to Mr. Fowler."

"You got it."

We skinned two of the snowshoes for the principal before we started for home. As he were pulling away Spunky muttered: "I wonder what he saw?"

Just then a large gray farm dog came out of the swamp and crossed the road ahead of us.

We laughed all the way home.

The Fishing Derby

Before the gang officially became the gang, most of the present members chummed around together so much that our neighbors and classmates referred to us as "the gang."

That was shortly after the Prohibition days and the era of Dillinger and Pretty Boy Floyd. When we officially formed the gang it caused a little stir in the neighborhood. Some of the older women would not stay on the town's only sidewalk when we were around.

The official formation of the gang was about the time Spunky Spriggs began helping out some of the elderly widows, especially Hestor Carmichael, who always needed some job done at her home. Mrs. Carmichael and others needed repair work done and didn't have the bread to hire someone to do it.

They quickly forgot about the time Brad Morrison almost set fire to the town. He was trying to burn out a family of skunks that occasionally made arithmetic lessons an odoriferous affair.

Country kids have their own way of life — at least we did. Skip Fisher, for instance, got his nickname because he wanted to build a canoe. He worked one whole summer hollowing and shaping an old tree that had been cut down and dragged to the end of the cow pasture by his dad.

At the time we wondered what he was doing. Brad, Spunky, and I hadn't seen him for a month. We were spending the summer fishing or bedeviling old Charley Thompson, the area's hermit who lived in a tilted house a mile from Spunky's place.

At first we didn't miss Skip, but he was the only one who could actually talk to Charley. We had been talking about Charley and wondering if he had any honeycombs that he could give us. We needed

Skip's help with Charley. So we gave up fishing the creek one day and walked the mile to Skip's house.

We asked his ma if Skip was sick or something and she told us he was out back near the woods working on a boat he was building.

"He's in the woods at the back of the cornfield. When you find him tell he's got to get his chores done."

We started out walking, but Spunky broke into a trot and by the time we neared the end of the corn we were at full gallop. Spunky was in the lead and when we got almost to the end, he motioned for us to stop.

"Let's sneak up on him and find out what he's doing before we let him know we're here," he said.

We found him 50 yards inside of the woods and watched him for 15 minutes before letting out a whoop and running the rest of the way. It looked like he was trying to hide something by throwing his shirt over a lump of something on the ground.

'Whatcha doing?" Brad asked.

"Yeh, whatcha hiding?" I chimed in.

Skip, normally bashful, did everything but stand on his head to get us to walk back to the house for some lemonade.

We wouldn't let him off that easy and before long we were looking down on Skip's project.

"Your ma said you was building a boat. That's not a boat, that's a canoe!"

"She don't know the difference."

"Does it float?"

"It floats, but I can't get it to stay upright. I got to sit on the left side — I mean way up on the left side to make the canoe stay on an even keel. Pa says the right side is heavier than the left and I've been scraping away trying to take off the extra weight.

"I didn't know logs could be heavier on one side than the other. My Pa says it ain't the log. I didn't get the inside even. . . there's more wood on one side than the other. I've been trying to shave it away with my chisel, but I don't know. It's more work than I thought it would be.

"He said he'll help me when the corn's in."

The sight of the partially built canoe was an inspiration to the rest of us and Brad, Spunky and I went to work building our own craft. We completed our craft in less than a month and field tested it on the pond back of Spunky's place.

It was so good we decided to enter the town's annual fishing derby on the town's lake. Any species counted and the heaviest catch would win half the entry money. The entry fee was $4 per boat. We asked Skip to join us because all we could come up with was $3.

It was a small lake and all of the contestants ferried their boats in the back of the pickup. We saw the boats sticking out over the back gate when Spunky's dad brought us to the derby. Everyone was laughing when we walked up to the entry table and put down our $4.

"I don't know if we can allow you into the derby," the mayor said. "We ain't never had a raft entered."

Spunky's dad assured the mayor that it was seaworthy and that before the contest started he would go home and get his boat in case it was needed to rescue us. Folks in our neck of the woods back then didn't use motors. Oars were their means of locomotion.

Spunky's dad got back 15 minutes later and we pushed our raft onto the lake. Most of the contestants rowed across the lake, but we stayed along the near shore and fished with cane poles baited with freshly dug earth worms.

The mayor fired his shotgun about noon. That gave the fishermen 15 minutes to get back to the launch site. You could fish as long as you wanted, but you had to be back within the 15 minutes.

We kept fishing and watched the other boats heading back. Some had already landed when Spunky's dad waved a red checkered handkerchief. We quickly poled into the shore in less than a minute.

Because we were the last "boat" in, our catch would be weighed last. The undertaker seemed to have the derby won with five bass weighing a little under 10 pounds.

"Let's see your catch — if you caught anything," the mayor said.

The four of us ran to the "boat" and each of us dragged a stringer of fish to the weigh-in.

I thought the undertaker was going to need his services. His face paled and he started to sputter when the needle of the scale with the weight of the 32 bluegills, three bass and a catfish pushed the needle full circle. Total weight was 12 1/2 pounds.

Each of us won $6 and our name was engraved on a plaque at City Hall.

Rafts were outlawed the following year.

Kerosene and Hot Tomatoes

E veryone thinks the gang is only involved in hunting and fishing, but that's far from the truth.

We are (kind of) like every outdoorsman in the world. We all
have special projects we get caught up in, especially if there is a
competitive slant to why someone suggests we get involved in this
or that.

Besides no one can fish or hunt seven days a week unless he or
she is a pay-for-hire guide — and then he or she is working for money,
which is a far cry from hunting and fishing just for pleasure.

It still surprised me when Spunky suggested at one of the gang's
meetings at the Slop Shop in February that everyone ante up a five
spot for a tomato growing contest. "The one who grows the first ripe
tomato of the year will win the pot and bragging rights for the year,"
Spunky said. "We all grow tomatoes and it could be a lot of fun."

"How in the world did you dream up that one?" Skip Fisher asked
amid the guffaws. "When did you start sniffing glue?"

Now Spunky doesn't like being the brunt of a joke and when his
eyebrows came together and started looking like a big mustache in
the middle of his forehead we all fell silent.

"You are getting old — the whole bunch of you." Spunky barked
"I just thought it would give us something different to do for the next
couple of months."

I told Spunky I'd rather go fishing, but the statement didn't slow
him down one bit.

"Hear me out, will you? We all know Bill Tremble. How he gets
excited about everything. Well, he and his friends have had a tomato
growing thing going on for years and he wins the prize almost every

year.

"I'm tired of hearing him brag about his early tomatoes. So I figured, if one of us could produce the first ripe tomato before he does, we could bring it to the Slop Shop and put it to him."

That's how the "First Ripe Tomato of the Season Contest" (FRTSC) started for the gang. It wasn't just growing tomatoes, but a contest with Tremble. Even so some of the gang didn't take the contest too seriously the first year.

The first pot was won by Fast Eddie Bresler and the rest of us were curious about how a non-farmer from Florida could win the prize.

It was a mystery until his wife, Ellie Mae, told my wife the tomato was grown in water in the high school chemistry lab during one of Fast Eddie's chemistry classes.

Of course we all cried foul, but Fast Eddie said no one said anything about rules or how the tomato had to be grown.

"The only thing Spunky said was that it could not be planted before April 1," Fast Eddie said.

Spunky, Fast Eddie, Skip Fisher and Brad Morrison picked up the prizes over the next nine years, but none of our sneaky efforts had ever beaten the date of Tremble's first tomato of the season.

I was the only one who hadn't won, a fact the gang discussed for my displeasure. Frankly, the desire to grow the first tomato of the season started to become an obsession to me. I don't know why, other than I don't like to be laughed at.

One year I was determined and began planning shortly after New Year's Day. I was so engrossed with the project that I neglected my work. Editors were calling and asking when I was going get off my duff and file the story I had promised.

My wife thought I was crazy on March 31, when I pulled into the yard with the back of my truck loaded with cow manure, a half dozen eight foot 2x2's and a large roll of plastic. I spent the rest of the day building a greenhouse.

"You're nuts," she greeted me when I came in for dinner. "There's still snow on the ground and you're building a greenhouse. Why?"

"Because this year I'm going to have the first ripe tomato of the season. That's why."

I didn't plant any of the tomatoes I had started in my office until the third day of the month — until the greenhouse had warmed a trifle. The first set of three died, but I had others growing on the front of my desk and they went into the ground on the 15th.

When the second group was planted I also placed two lighted kerosene lanterns in the enclosure. A week later the plants were thriving. They were doing better than I was because my wife made me change clothes on the back porch before I came into the kitchen. My clothes reeked of kerosene.

The gang had a fishing day planned for the month of June and I insisted they all meet at my house for breakfast. After eating I told them I had something to show them and led them to my little garden.

There in all their glory were two red tomatoes growing on plants higher than they had grown before. Green tomatoes were bunched on the branches ready to mature in another week or so.

Of course the greenhouse had been taken down and all of the post holes, plastic and lanterns were nowhere to be seen.

I received the FRTSC award a week later at the Slop Shop. The gang was elated. I gave a couple of tomatoes to each of the gang three weeks before Tremble's group produced a red tomato.

On the way out the door Brad told me that he thought he got a whiff of kerosene when I handed him his tomatoes.

First I thought it came from the tomatoes," he said. "But who ever heard of tomatoes smelling of kerosene."

My wife was asleep when I got home. I gently shook her into awareness — but not to say goodnight, but to call her "Snitch."

The Cousin and Fast Eddie

I'm not superstitious, but a lucky jacket is a lucky jacket. There's no getting away from it. I catch more fish when I'm wearing the denim jacket I wore the day I slew the steelhead on the AuSable River a dozen years ago when no one else around caught a single fish.

It's not easy getting out of the house with my denim jacket when I go trout fishing. There's always a comment like: "You're not going to wear that dirty, holes-in-the-elbows jacket again, are you?"

"Now Mary, there's nothing wrong with this jacket. It's just broken in and it's got a certain odor about it that makes the fish go crazy," I always counter.

"You bet it smells. You could pass for the biggest spawn bag in Michigan."

The discussion always comes to an end when I throw the jacket into the back of the truck. At least I think it does because I can't hear much over the roar of the old truck motor.

"I'm going to pick up Spunky," I hollered and pulled out of the yard. It's funny she didn't wave. I could see her outlined against the light in the kitchen and she didn't wave. She always waves.

Spunky was out in front of his place when I got there.

"It feels like it's going to stay cold," he said climbing into the cab of the truck. "If that's the case, there won't be any hatches and we'll have to fish bait."

"Just like always," I said.

Heck, Spunky fishes bait even when there is a hatch. I suppose it's because he can't pronounce the fancy names real trout fishermen put on bugs.

Ethel's diner was crowded when we stopped for breakfast. Spunky stood just inside of the door and surveyed the crowd.

"Where's Fast Eddie?" he asked. "I thought he'd be here by now."

"He's not stopping," I said. "He's bringing his wife's cousin and said he didn't think the guy would like Ethel's. He's going to meet us at the river."

"What's wrong with Ethel's?"

"Nothing, but the cousin is a big wheel at some company in Pennsylvania. I suppose he's used to eating at expensive places — you know the kind that have table cloths and all that."

Spunky was half way through his western omelet and double order of hash browns when he put his knife and fork down.

"There's nothing wrong with Ethel's," he said. "Dig in, it's getting late."

I pulled the truck off the road and far enough into a stand of pines so that it couldn't be seen by passersby. Our logic was that there was no sense in letting others know about our hotspots.

"I thought Fast Eddie would have been here ahead of us," I said shouldering myself into my denim jacket.

"You still got that ratty old jacket," Spunky commented "I thought Mary would have thrown it out long ago. You smell awful."

"Never mind. Me and this jacket are going to catch our limit this morning. I put some worms in those two boxes — one for you and one for me."

As I finished speaking headlights appeared bouncing through the opening between the pines. Fast Eddie parked his truck in a clump of bushes and got out. A second person emerged from the other side of the truck.

"My Gawd, what is it?" Spunky gasped. "It looks like one of them models in the L.L. Bean catalog.'

"Don't say that out loud, you may hurt Fast Eddie's feelings."

"I'll try, but I don't know if I'll be able to control myself."

It took several minutes for Fast Eddie and the cousin to get their gear together and walk over to where we were waiting.

"This is my wife's cousin-in-law, Ian McPhearson," Fast Eddie said as they approached.

We shook hands and Spunky and I studied the man standing before us.

He was dressed in waders, a forest green turtle neck sweater showed over the starched collar of an immaculate tan fishing jacket.

He also sported a hat festooned with a couple of dozen flies of various colors. He was smoking one of those big bent pipes — the kind that Sherlock Holmes smoked.

"What hatch do you expect this morning," he asked right off.

"The usual," Spunky said before I had a chance to answer the cousin's question.

"What Spunky means is that we hope for the usual early emerging species," I quickly butted in. "Like the Baetis vagans, Empherella suvaria and Leptophlebia."

Spunky gasped, but Ian never batted an eye as I rattled off the litany.

"It's a pleasure to meet a man who appreciates the niceties of trout fishing," Ian said. "They are even hard to find on the best rivers of Scotland these days."

Spunky groaned audibly while Ian rummaged through a fly pouch as though he hadn't heard a thing.

"I think I'll start with a Blue-Wing Olive, Hendrickson or Black Quill and keep watching for other species that might appear if it warms up enough for them."

"Well, let's get to it," I said, shoving the small tin of worms deeper into my jacket pocket.

"What's that fishy smell," I heard the cousin ask Fast Eddie as the two of them headed upstream.

Spunky and I weren't 25 yards from Fast Eddie and the cousin before he grabbed my arm.

"What's with you? You never told me about any beaten virgins, or whatever you called them — and I'm your best friend."

I gave Spunky my best grimace, the kind I used to save for students, when I was teaching Journalism in college. "All that stuff I told Ian is on a need to know basis and I figured you never needed to know."

Spunky fished a worm out of the can, threaded it on a No.12 hook and floated it into a tangle of roots at the river's edge. His abrupt turn signaled the end of the conversation.

Fishing was bad. A small brookie was the only fish I saw in three hours on the river. Spunky managed three small rainbows before he caught up to me downstream. He seemed to be over his pout.

"It's too cold," Spunky said. "I haven't seen many fish moving around. Where'd you learn all the Latin. I suppose it is Latin or Greek stuff you were telling L.L. Bean?"

"Poor Ian," I said, "he's not going to be too happy with Michigan trout fishing. I'll bet he's been thinking about Scotland and its rivers all morning. Rivers where you can backcast a ton and not have to worry about snagging trees and brush along the bank. I didn't see any hatches either.

"Don't let my conversation with Ian bother you. I've got to confess that I wouldn't know that an Emhpemerella subvaria was a mayfly if I hadn't researched it for an article I wrote a few years back.

"And I remembered this morning. I'm a lot like you — a Noctis Onhiskneeis."

"What the heck is that?"

"A nightcrawler."

"You're kidding."

"No, it was something my dad taught me. We better get back to the truck. Trout fishing's going to keep until the weather warms up."

It took 15 minutes to walk back to the truck and we weren't suprised to see Fast Eddie and the cousin waiting for us. Fast Eddie seemed excited about something.

"How'd you do?," I asked.

"Limited out in a couple of hours after Ian found that the trout went bonkers over a Whirling Dun."

"I have to thank you Herb," the cousin said seriously. "If you hadn't told me what I could expect, I doubt we would have done any good, but you didn't mention how difficult it would be to cast a fly with all the brush.

"It took me an hour to teach Fast Eddie the roll cast and then it was duck soup as you Yankees say. He caught on real quick. You ought to have seen him roll a fly to a particular spot."

Ian sniffed the air: "There must be a dead fish around here. I smelled it just before we started fishing this morning."

I threw the jacket into the truck and told Fast Eddie and Ian we were stopping at Ethel's for lunch and they were welcome to join us. Fast Eddie said he had to get home, but Ian talked him into joining us.

"My treat," Ian said. "It's the least I can do after all your help this morning."

They beat us to Ethel's because it took a few minutes to find a trash can where I deposited my jacket. Ian turned out to be a nice guy. The locals still talk about the dude at Ethel's, but Spunky and I seldom join in.

The Gang's Police Record

I think it was Skip Fisher who suggested we begin a conserva tion program to help restore the pheasant population in our area back to the glory years of the late 40's and 50's. The gang was gung ho and told him to look into the matter with whatever state department was involved in giving us a license to promote the project.

He made calls and sent inquiries to several state agencies and departments and received a fist full of papers to be filled out.

At a meeting, three or four months later at the Slop Shop, he showed us the papers and said there were a lot of questions that had to be answered. There was even a question about whether or not any of the people who would be officers in the undertaking had a criminal record.

"I was going to answer 'NO' to that question on all of the queries, but I thought I'd better ask all of you first," Skip said.

"Well, I agree that we don't have to worry about any of us having a police record," I said. "Let's get cracking on the rest of the questions."

"I thought one of you mentioned that Spunky had been taken in by the sheriff a number of times for driving while under the influence," Fast Eddie Bresler piped up.

"I ought to wipe your mouth out with soap," Spunky blurted. "I spent some hours in the county jail off and on when one of the young deps stopped me for speeding and thought I had been drinking.

"I want you to know — AND DON'T YOU FORGET — that I have never been arrested for anything, Even if I was, it wouldn't mean a damn thing. They're looking for things like murder, robbery or sex crimes.

"You can answer no. No one in this group has a criminal record.

Period."

Being as I had made my living as a reporter, I was watching every member of the gang for their reaction to the question and Spunky's response. That's why I asked Brad Morrison:

"You feeling all right? Your face looks flushed."

'I'm okay," he said.

We spent the rest of the evening reading the various questions from the authors of the questionnaire and decided that setting up an organization was more work than we wanted to get into.

I was finishing a second cup of coffee the next morning when I saw Brad Morisson's car pull into the driveway and was waiting for him on the back porch.

"Hi Herb, got a cup of coffee?" he asked as he got out of the car.

"Sure, come on in."

Brad said hello to my wife and fidgeted: "Can we talk in your office?"

"You look worried? Something wrong?"

"It was the meeting last night," he began once my wife was out of hearing. "I'm glad we decided to dump the foundation idea. I was worried for awhile."

"What's to worry about?"

"That question about if anyone of us had been arrested."

"Hey none of us . . . are you trying to tell me you've been arrested?"

"Sort of — let me tell you what happened.

"It happened while I was downstate and I volunteered to help a fund drive for my church. Anyway I was given the names of 25 parishioners to call on. I was half way through my responsibility when it happened.

"I had to call on an elderly lady parishioner. She lived on the second floor of an apartment building and when I knocked on the door a woman's voice from inside shouted: 'get away or I'll call the police."

"I told her through the door who I was and why I was calling — that Father Myers had asked me to visit her, and all she said to that was — 'get away from the door." Well, I backed up and started for the stairs. I heard the door open.

"The next thing I know this old woman is coming at me with a frying pan. I ran down the stairs with her right behind me. I got to the front door, but it was one of those that need a key or a buzzer to open from either side.

"I felt the wind from the frying pan passing my head and started to run down the first floor hallway. She was right behind me. When I couldn't get out the back door either, I climbed the stairs and passed her door again.

"I was getting winded. Halfway down the stairs the woman caught up to me and swung the frying pan. It hit me on the shoulder. I was slowing down, really slowing down. And she kept swinging the pan. She didn't seem to be getting weary or anything."

"The third time I got to the front door a policeman was waiting for me with a drawn pistol. He slammed me against the wall and handcuffed me.

"Just before he shoved me out the door I saw the women. No wonder she didn't get tired there were two of them — twins sisters.

"I explained to the cop who I was and why I was there and told him to call my pastor. The next thing I know I'm being fingerprinted and charged with assault, sexual assault and resisting arrest. They dropped all charges the next day, but I was arrested and spent a night in jail.

"Now you see why last night's discussion really bothered me."

I managed not to laugh until the end of the Brad's story. "Who would think of the mild mannered, soft speaking church-going Brad Morrison as a sex deviate," I said.

"You won't tell anyone will you?" Brad pleaded.

"You got my word on it."

The Mother Complex

B e careful, be certain, be cautious are phrases which should be incorporated into every marriage ceremony — no matter if the ceremony is in church, city hall or wherever weddings are performed these days.

Being cognizant of the phrases makes for a successful marriage. That's true, no matter which side of the matrimonial aisle you stood on when you took the plunge.

My being careful is what I credit for a successful marriage of more than 50 years ago. That's why I refused to go with Fast Eddie on a morel mushroom picking expedition on Mother's Day.

He's the reason I got my fifth or sixth lesson in being cautious, It started when I thought it sounded respectful when Fast Eddie called his wife, Ellie Mae — Mother — and I tried it out at home.

When I called my wife Mother, it went over like a streaker at a church synod, let me tell you. Mary didn't get angry or raise her voice. All she said was: "Don't you ever call me Mother again. I'm not your mother, I'm your wife."

The next sound was the slamming of the bedroom door.

The incident was as fresh as the day it happened when Fast Eddie Bresler asked me to take him to my recently discovered morel mushroom picking area on Mother's Day.

Now, I'd do just about anything for Fast Eddie, but not on Mother's Day. I didn't tell him the real reason for not going, but told him all of the kids called on Mother's Day and I wanted to talk to them too.

I did get out the county map and marked the spot along a sandy road that serves as a firebreak through some Federal Land and followed that with some expert advice.

"Make sure you take a compass reading when you walk into the woods and walk out the opposite direction from the one you walked in on."

Fast Eddie who was a greenhorn in the woods at the time — and still is — thanked me profusely and said he understood why I couldn't go along.

Mary and I were sitting down to a grilled steak when Ellie Mae, Fast Eddie's wife, skidded her car to a stop a few feet from the porch.

"Herb, Fast Eddie hasn't come home. He said he'd be home by noon, she ranted hysterically. "I told him not to go alone. I just know he's lost or broken his leg or something."

It took several minutes to calm her down. Mary was very solicitous and told her not to worry.

"Herb will find him."

I called Spunky Spriggs , the best woodsman I know, to enlist his aid. He said he'd be at my house in five minutes and that he was pretty sure we would find him — if he's lost.

"That's a pretty tricky section with lots of wet areas and besides that road doesn't run the way it looks," he added

"I know that," I said somewhat testily. "I didn't think he'd go far enough into the woods to get to where it makes the turn."

Fast Eddie's small truck was right where I told him to park when I mapped out the area for him. I looked down the road at the 90 degree turn in the road a quarter of a mile from where his car was parked. From where we stood looking at it you couldn't tell the road turned.

I told Spunky it took me a few minutes of study to pick up the sharp bend in the road when I picked morels in the same spot earlier in the week.

"It's a good thing you didn't range too far or you would have been the one I was looking for," Spunky said. "Blow the horn, I suspect he might be calling for help by now. If he answers we might get a fix on him."

I held my thumb on the horn for a long time on several attempts. We listened, but there was no response.

Spunky agreed with my assessment of the situation — that Fast Eddy was somewhere west of where we found his truck — possibly walking parallel to the road after it made the turn. We headed for the turn in the road.

We made several stops and blew the horn without getting any

response. Although I didn't voice my concern I was worried that Fast Eddie had fallen and broken a leg or got stuck in some of the swampy areas.

"Maybe we ought to take a hike and call as we go," I suggested. "We've come a long way."

"We'll stay on the road for another mile or so," Spunky said. "If we get into the woods . . . well it would be like looking for needle in a haystack. And right now we don't know which haystack he's in."

We were more than a mile down the road when we thought we heard a thin voice respond to the horn.

"I think there's an old logging grade about 100 yards back," I ventured. "We can walk in on that and see if it's him."

Ten minutes later the sweat was pouring down my back. We hadn't heard any response to our calls for several minutes, but Spunky insisted that we keep walking along the grade deeper into the woods.

We climbed to the top of a large hill and called again. The wind whipping along the crest dried the perspiration and I was beginning to feel a little better.

Spunky let out a yell — a countrified version of stentorian blast. Instantly we recognized Fast Eddie's voice somewhere down in the swamp at the base of the hill, but it took several more calls and 15 minutes before we saw him walking toward us at the base of the hill.

"Am I glad to see you guys," Fast Eddie said 10 minutes later when he fell at our feet on top of the hill. "I'm bushed, but look at all the morels I found."

Spunky gave him a drink of water out of his canteen and we lay on the hilltop while Fast Eddie rested for the walk back to my truck. Spunky checked over the morels and put them into two piles.

"You did pretty good," he told Fast Eddie. "Most of them are real, but these six aren't edible."

"They all look the same to me," Fast Eddie said.

Spunky held one of each and pointed out the difference between a true and a false morel mushroom.

"Eat one of these babies and you could cash it all in," he told Fast Eddie.

"How'd you get so wet," I quickly asked to get Fast Eddie's mind off what could have happened if Spunky hadn't found the false morels.

"I was doing what you told me. I walked north and about 11 a.m. I started to walk south — my gosh that was four hours ago — but I didn't come to the road. I got a little excited and decided to walk through some of the wet areas instead of going around them.

"Mother will have a fit when she sees what I did to my new jeans."

I put my arm around his shoulder and counseled him about the necessity of being careful when dealing with a spouse. In fact I explained everything, including the sound of a slamming door.

I also told him that he should have used more caution before walking into the woods.

"If you had, you would have seen that the road you were parked on changes from and east-west road to a north-south road. You're lucky Spunky and I figured out what happened and cut you off before you walked to Lansing."

"You two guys are great — figuring all that out. I only hope that someday I'll be as good in the woods as you two are."

"Did you happen to come across that big beaver dam at the edge of the cedar swamp about a half mile south of here?" I asked.

Spunky's head whipped around and he stared at me and his mouth began making funny noises.

"Be careful, Spunky," I said quietly so Fast Eddie couldn't hear. "Whatever you're thinking, don't say it. And don't slam the door of my truck when you get in."

We watched Fast Eddie leave for home after telling him to be sure he called his wife at his house or mine when he got to the first telephone available.

I was about to start the truck when Spunky pulled the keys from the ignition.

"We ain't going nowhere until you tell me how you knew about that loggin' grade, the beaver pond and the swamp," he said with his eyes riveted on me.

"As you know I have a lot of topographical maps and . . ."

"Save that for your readers. Admit it. You got lost the first time you picked morels there and you walked out on the same line that Fast Eddie used."

I hated what I had to say, but the truth is the truth.

"Both times."

Cars , Home Repairs and Oatmeal

They don't make cars the way they used to when I was a young man.

At least that's the what the experts tell me. The experts in this case are my gang — Brad Morrison, Skip Fisher, and most expert of them all, Spunky Spriggs.

And it's a good thing they don't make cars the way they used to because my non-expertise doesn't show through like it once did. For years the gang got their kicks when my car or truck would suddenly develop a fever and I tried to fix it myself.

The normal pattern was to work on the car for a day or two and when the patient didn't respond to my tinkering, I'd call Spunky. He'd call the rest of the gang and they would descend on my place like a swarm of locusts.

In a way it was good because I didn't have to pay any mechanic's fee, just buy the brew and an odd part once in awhile, but now I have to take the truck or my wife's car to a mechanic who is a certified and trained technician.

You know what I mean. A guy who wires your car up to a machine and attaches wires to every part of the engine while reading an instruction booklet or manual of some sort.

I can hear him yet, saying things like: "It's worse than I thought. Your whatchamajigger isn't kicking out enough voltage to engage the computer properly and that's got the timing off, or you need a new rheostature or something and that he'll have to order it because he doesn't have any in stock."

"How long?" I ask.

"Probably two or three days. It won't take much time to install once I get the part. Part runs $20 and the labor is $35.50."

Then we go around and around because I can't understand how something that costs $20 and won't take long to install carries such a large labor charge. Eventually the mechanic points to a book and says: "See, here it is — installation fee $33.50. Says so right here in the book."

"Cars sure have changed," Spunky said. "That's why I still drive my old fashioned truck. I understand how to fix it."

While I was waiting for the rheostature, or whatever it was that my truck needed, I thought of Old Man Claghorn. I mentioned him to Spunky who had dropped in to see how I was getting along without wheels, restricted to the back porch and working on "honey do" projects.

"I almost forgot about Claghorn," Spunky said and laughed. "What was his front name? I forget.

"Raymond, that's it. I almost forgot about Claghorn. He was a piece of fruitcake, wasn't he?"

The inactivity, except household chores made me a little sour and I huffed out an answer.

"How should I know. I never saw or heard anything from or about the Claghorns since they moved?"

Spunky shook his head and said he wouldn't bet that Claghorn hadn't killed his son, Spence, in the interim. "Not that he'd kill him intentionally, but one of Claghorn's hair brained schemes could have done him in.

"Remember the time he was painting his three story house on Deer Street and his ladder wouldn't reach to the peak?"

"Yeah, he wouldn't buy an extension for the ladder because he didn't know anyone who had an extension ladder long enough to finish the job so he had to improvise."

We remember that day like it was yesterday. Spunky, Skip and I were still in high school and were walking to the creek the other side of town to fish bass when we saw Claghorn shove a 10-inch wide plank out an attic window.

We stopped and watched as Spence, about 13 years old at the time crawled out onto it.

We could see his knees knocking from across the road, especially when he bent down to lap up some paint from the bucket Claghorn had shoved out on the plank after him.

When Spence had finished painting the peak, he started back into the attic, but was told by his pa to stay there while he checked the job.

A minute later Claghorn came out of the house and looked up at the peak. He made Spence lean one way and the other so that he could see the entire peak. He began cussing Spence because he missed a couple of spots. We forgot about fishing and spent the whole afternoon watching Spence finish painting the two peaks of the house.

During recess at school the next day we told Spence he had a lot of guts to crawl out and paint the house and he said it was "Nuthin," and that his pa was always figuring things for him to do at home.

Spunky and I have always been lucky as far as the Claghorns were concerned. We often heard his father telling Spence that a man could do anything if he put his mind to it.

Funny thing, and a good one too, was the fact that Spence never got hurt, not a scratch, no matter what Claghorn thought up for him to do, but he never let him touch his car.

A week before they moved to Colorado, Spunky and I were going to the same creek to do some frogging when we saw Claghorn fussing with his car. The hood was up and he was messing with the radiator. He started the car and let it run for a while. He looked under the hood and studied the radiator from all angles, including from under the car.

"No leaks," he shouted to his wife who was sitting on the front porch. That should do it. I'm going into town."

He backed the car into the street and drove about 50 yards when we heard a BOOM. Steam was pouring out from under the car. Old man Claghorn jumped out of the car and pulled on the hood latch.

As the hood rose, the steam swirled around his upper body and he started to cuss a blue streak. He ran to the house yelling to his wife that he was burned and ordered her to get some cold water for his face and hands.

Spunky and I walked over to the car. A pasty substance covered the motor, the under side of the hood and was trickling to the ground.

"Oatmeal," Spunky said. "He tried to plug the leaks with oatmeal. Looks like he used the whole box."

Five Thumbs Award

S everal years ago the gang established a fly tying contest be
fore the opening of the trout season. Everyone in the gang
had won at least once except me.

The reason I hadn't won was because between good intentions
and completion of the task my thumbs behaved like a three-year-old
at the dentist's office.

Every year they awaited my entry with baited breath. Normally
that should be written as bated breath—sort of like gasping while
waiting for something to happen. It was so bad that every year I
bought a round of suds at the Slop Shop instead of entering the contest.

The second year of my hiatus from the contest the gang presented
me with the five thumbs award. It consisted of a hand with five thumbs
and some drivel under the crude plaster thingamajig about it being
an award for someone who has no talent at all.

I responded that if I had any talent at all I would be a brain sur-
geon, but having none I opted to be a writer. One of my granddads
asked me once why I was a writer and I told him it was because I
couldn't do anything else.

Well, the year I'm going to tell you about was a surprise to everyone, including me. It's not that I'm cheap, but I had decided that I
wasn't going to treat a round and would produce a fly good enough
to be considered an entry.

The night of the contest my wife kept calling to me from the top
of the cellar stairs to let me know the guys were at the Slop Shop and
waiting for their brew. After an hour of nagging (my wife prefers to
call it urging) I emerged from the cellar with not one, but a dozen

quasi-streamers in a range of color from red to violet.

My wife laughed at the gaudy colors arrayed in a soft fly case.

"You don't think you're going to win with one of those," she chided. "Spunky can do better with his eyes closed."

We've been married too long to consider divorce, but I thought of it on the drive into town.

"Now we can get started," Brad Morrison said as I walked through the side door. "Herb's ready to buy and we can get the judging started.

"Not so fast. I happen to have not one, but 12 flies to place in the competition," I said, and dumped the dozen streamers on the table for all to see. Skip Fisher was the first to grab the pouch of streamers.

"H'mm, they almost look like flies, but they are merely imitations of the imitations most of us use," he said. "I give you "A" for effort, but as a former college professor you know that ain't enough."

Spunky, my best friend in the gang, waved his hand for order and demanded the other entries be placed on the table. He also ordered a round because he said he been too busy to tie any flies for the contest.

"You know the rules," he said glaring at everyone at the table. "No entries, you buy a round."

Before the evening ended Brad's Caddis Worm was judged the best in show and my collection of streamers was awarded second place, the first time second place ever was recognized.

At the conclusion of the judging, Spunky said he had a motion to make, and without waiting for any approval, he proposed a new rule to the effect that every fly tyer must fish his fly on opening day.

That brought some hoots from the gang, but Spunky is a presence, even to us, and on opening day on a local stream Spunky inspected our fly boxes to make sure we weren't bringing in any "professional" flies.

Before daylight the gang dispersed and went to favorite spots on the river. I was fishing an inside curve, letting my streamer skitter along the edge of a submerged log. I usually make several passes at a hole and move on to the next hotspot, but the red, white and blue streamer snagged up on the first run past the log.

I tightened my line, jiggled the rod tip to dislodge the streamer and was surprised when the line started to move toward the middle of the river. Five minutes later a I slid my net under a 12-inch rainbow and shouted "Hallelujah."

I had just caught the first fish on a home-tied fly in the gang's history. Before the morning was over and we gathered for lunch and a look-see at what everyone caught, I had put one brook trout and two rainbows in my creel.

It seems fishing was tough and the grand total, including my four, was six trout. A peacock never strutted as pompously as I did that morning. Everyone wanted to know what my secret was and how I had become such and expert at fly tying.

Let me tell you I was obnoxious. I demanded to know by what authority Spunky demanded to know all my secrets.

His answered: "Because I'm bigger than you are and I'll drive you into that ant hill if you won't tell us."

That convinced me I should "fess" up.

"Look, I am a guy with five thumbs when it comes to doing anything which requires skill. Why do you think I became a writer? I saw this ad for some miracle glue and got an idea that maybe I could build a fly without having to tie "x" number of knots that I know nothing about.

"All I did was spread some miracle glue on the hook and wind different colored yard around and around the part I had glued. I hate to admit this, but I was tired of buying drinks because I couldn't tie a fly. With my system, I didn't have to tie a knot."

Two months later they gave me a Five Thumbs plaque which read:

"Five thumbs, no talent, but he is the glue that holds our gang together."

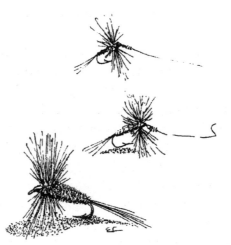

Of Mice and Fast Eddie

E llie Mae Bresler is a lady — a Southern Lady if you please.
Her compliments about recipes, people and even Fast Eddie
Bresler, her husband, fairly drip with honey. She also is kind to ani-
mals, even the one's most people consider pests.

She's kind to everyone she meets, even the gang Fast Eddie has
become addicted to, but I sometimes sense that there's a little reser-
vation when it comes to the gang.

It's not that she doesn't like Spunky Spriggs, Brad Morrison, Skip
Fisher and yours truly. It's just that she looks a little different at the
gang that taught her husband to fish and hunt.

One afternoon I saw Fast Eddie's truck turn into the drive and
told my wife to put another pot of coffee on. "We got visitors, Fast
Eddie and Ellie Mae."

Right off he hit me with a problem that he and Ellie Mae were
groping with.

A few minutes later Mary poured four cups of coffee and invited
Ellie Mae to sit in the parlor where "we can be more comfortable and
not have to listen to old fishing or hunting stories."

"Herb, I need your help again," Fast Eddie said as soon as the
women had left the kitchen. "My problem is mice and I don't want
Ellie Mae to know I've talked to you about this problem. I'd like to
consider this conversation private."

I hollered to my wife that Fast Eddie and I were going down to
my workshop because I wanted him to look at a new bass lure I was
working on. She hollered back that I should show him some of my
early ones and point out how pretty they looked floating on their
backs.

Fast Eddie followed me down to the basement and waited patiently for me to dig out the bottle of Old Crow from its hiding place and pour a drop or two into our coffee.

"That's better," I said after a sip of the enhanced coffee. "What's this about mice?"

"We have mice in the house and I've tried everything to get rid of them, but nothing works."

I struck a fatherly pose and told him that it takes time to eliminate a house of mice, especially if there are a lot of the critters running around.

"You can't get rid of them overnight. You have to keep setting traps day after day until you've killed them all."

"You've hit the problem on the head," Fast Eddie said. "Ellie Mae doesn't want me to kill them. She thinks mice are 'cute,' except when they are in the house. Those are her exact words. All she wants me to do is get them out of the house."

Fast Eddie explained that he had live trapped mice by the dozens and released them out back of his garage, but thinks they are getting back into the house because he traps two or three every night.

"Hey that's easy," I told him. "Release them on your way to work — about halfway between your house and the high school. Your problems will be over as soon as you trap the last one."

"Do you think so?"

"Trust me. I'm an old mouse catcher from way back. If you follow my advice, your mouse problem is over. It may take some time, but eventually, you will run out of mice."

A week later Fast Eddie was back at the house soliciting more mouse advice.

"I thought my problems were over. I had been catching two or three mice every night and dumping them the next morning near the abandoned Jenkin's farm three miles from home — that's about half way to the high school.

"Finally I went three days without catching one and thought the problem was over. I didn't set a trap for three nights and on the fourth night I set five traps. I was shocked because four of the traps had mice in them.

"The mice had eaten all the bait and I dumped them again at the Jenkins place on my way to work. It's where I had dropped the others. There was nothing in the traps the next morning, but I set them again last night expecting to come up empty.

"I was surprised to see mice in three of the five traps. And Herb, I think one of them is a mouse I'd caught before because it has a blondish patch on its right side. What am I going to do?"

"Eddie, you're imagining things. Think about it.

"Does it seem reasonable to you that the mice traveled almost three miles back to your place?"

"No, but that mouse with the blondish patch sure looked like one I'd trapped before."

I motioned for Fast Eddie to follow me to the basement. After a few seconds of rummaging through my cluttered paint closet, I handed him a spray can. The pink paint was left over after I spray painted a coloring box for one my granddaughters.

"If you catch any more, spray a little paint on their backs," I advised. "I guarantee you will not see those mice again."

Three days later I was having breakfast when my wife said: "Fast Eddie just turned into the driveway. What are you borrowing from him now? He's carrying a burlap sack."

Fast Eddie looked perplexed when he showed me four live traps with a mouse in each of them. Three of the four had a splotch of pink paint on its back.

"What'll I do now?" he asked.

"Leave the traps here and pick them up on your way home. I'll take care of the rest, but tell Ellie Mae you dumped them off at the usual place."

Fast Eddie dropped mice off three more times before he stopped catching any more in his live traps.

It was the last I heard of the Bresler mice until a dinner party two months later. I had to listen to Ellie Mae coo over how bright her husband was to get rid of all the mice without killing any of them.

Pictures Don't Lie Or Do They?

Pictures don't lie. Right? Don't count on it.

The gang's problem with pictures developed (pardon the pun) on one of the gang's annual trips to fish the backwaters of the Manistee River behind Tippy Dam a short drive from the city of Manistee in the western portion of Michigan's Lower Peninsula.

Spunky Spriggs, Brad Morrison, Skip Fisher, Fast Eddie Bresler and I had fished the Tippy Dam impoundment for northern pike from sunup to sundown for five days with only a modicum of success.

Oh, we caught enough legal pike to satisfy the appetites of the five of us, but we didn't hang on to any fish of bragging size. The cameras stayed in the carrying cases for the entire trip and we were heading home when we saw three guys standing on the High Bridge near Wellston with a stringer of healthy fish.

Naturally Spunky and I stopped our trucks to take a close look at the five northerns the trio were taking pictures of. The fish were in the above 10-pound class and made our mouths drool.

One of the trio asked if we would take a picture of them holding up their fish.

"Only two of us can get into the picture, but if one of you would take a couple of shots all three of us could be in it.

"Sure," Spunky said. "Herb here is a professional outdoor writer/ photographer and I'm sure he can oblige."

I was flattered by Spunky's description of me and spent the next 10 minutes posing and photographing the trio. The guys thanked me and we were about to leave when Fast Eddie asked the fishermen if they minded if he had his picture taken with the fish.

"Be our guest," one of the trio said and I wasted another five minutes getting pictures of Fast Eddie and the fish with his camera. Before I finished the rest of the gang joined Fast Eddie and I took pictures of the four of them with the fish.

Before we got back into our vehicles Spunky motioned for us to huddle up before we continued our journey.

"This is more for Fast Eddie than anyone else," he began. "but I want to remind everyone that we never have or never will claim we took fish we didn't catch. Some fishermen I know may think we don't catch all of the fish that we do, but we don't steal anyone's fish — not even on film."

I forgot all about the pictures over the next few weeks until I got a call from Spunky for a special meeting of the gang to discuss an important "fish picture" matter. He said he was going to call the rest of the gang and hoped we could meet that night.

Spunky was waiting when I arrived and the entire gang, including Fast Eddie, showed up in the next 30 minutes. I had never seen Spunky so solemn or agitated.

Eileen O'Conner, the barmaid at the Slop Shop also appeared agitated when she took our drink orders and grumbled something about rollers skates because we were as far away from the bar as we could get without being outside on the sidewalk.

"We've got something serious to discuss and I don't want you — the town crier — to hear what we're saying," he told her when she brought the drinks to the table.

"Hey, get down off your high horse," Brad cut him off before he could say anything else. "What are you picking on Eileen for and what's this all about?"

"Someone's violated our code of ethics, and we've got to decide whether that someone can continue as a member of the gang," Spunky said in a voice so soft that we had to strain to hear him.

"Fast Eddie, what do you have say for yourself?"

"About what?"

"About this picture of you standing on High Bridge with a stringer of five pike. I found it in the teachers' union newspaper. The caption says: "Pictures don't lie.""

"Let me see that!" Fast Eddie shouted.

Well, Fast Eddie never shouts, but the volume was up a tad from his usual speech pattern.

Spunky threw the paper at him and glared.

Fast Eddie studied the newspaper, and when he raised his eyes there were tears forming in the corner of his eyes.

"I don't know where they got that picture. I didn't give it to them. I showed the picture once — to my class at the high school ... and told them they belonged to someone else.

"I explained about the other men and how they asked if we could take their picture ... and because the pike were the biggest I have ever seen ... I asked the men if I could have my picture taken with the fish.

"So help me. I don't know how this got into the newspaper. I keep the picture on my desk at school and dream of catching something like that.

"As far as I know the picture has never left my desk. Give me a little time and I'll find out and let you know how it happened."

That said Fast Eddie headed straight for the door. The door was slammed shut and he was gone.

Two days later Fast Eddie stopped by to tell me how the picture got in his union's newspaper. He explained that the principal had seen the picture on his desk one evening after a school open house and decided to write cutlines and surprise me by getting it into the teacher's newspaper.

"And I was SURPRISED in capital letters." Fast Eddie said.

"Will you help me square it with Spunky?"

The Class Reunion

Class reunions are wonderful events. It is not only the party itself, but the weeks and months leading up to the bash which adds nostalgia and wonderment to the affair.

At least that's how it was years ago before our 20th high school reunion for Spunky Spriggs, Brad Morrison, Skip Fisher and myself.

The reunion for the four of us began to take shape at the Slop Shop, our local watering hole. Spunky first brought it up the day the mailman delivered the announcement of the reunion.

"I wonder if Gretchen will make it to the reunion," Spunky said over a cold one. "I'll bet she's still a knockout. I still dream of her once in a while."

His words brought pictures of Gretchen Schmittler swinging down the corridor of the old high school and I wished I had been fortunate enough to dream of Gretchen occasionally.

"I don't know," I said. "She's never come to any of the reunions and time has a way of changing all of us. You're heavier, except for your hair, than you were when you graduated."

"Hey who's calling the pot black. At least everyone will recognize me."

There was a tinge of ice in his voice as he spoke.

That was the start of our reunion. We talked about everyone in the class over the next two months. It doesn't take long to run through a class of 42 students.

Even so, there were a couple of classmates we couldn't talk about for very long. Every class has them. Kids you went to school with, but didn't socialize with for a variety of reasons.

In Spunky's case, if you didn't hunt or fish, you may as well have gone to school in Europe. No sir, if you didn't hunt or fish, Spunky wouldn't remember them — with the exception of Gretchen Schmittler.

There were three we couldn't remember, except vaguely. Kathleen Browner and John Fletcher were total blanks. The name, Walter Schrodink rang a bell because everyone called him "Dink" for short.

Spunky remembered that some of our classmates called him the runt because he looked like he was the runt of the litter.

The reunion was a big success. It was held at the local Knights of Columbus Hall. Only four of our classmates didn't attend, Gretchen Schmittler, Kathleen Browner, John Fletcher and Walter Schrodink.

The only one sorely missed was Gretchen and Spunky went into a funk for a month because she was a no-show.

We were holding our fourth or fifth re-run of the reunion for Fast Eddie Bresler and Spunky was in the middle of a discussion about how Mrs. Dressler, our English teacher, had berated me for a grammar error in one of my fishing stories, when he stopped in mid-sentence.

"What's the old coot doing in the Slop Shop?" he asked.

All heads swung in the direction of the thin gray-haired man headed toward our table.

"Evenin' boys," the old coot said. "I wonder if I could buy you boys a round?"

"Well, sure Tom — I mean Mr. Conklin," I said, "but what brings you to the Slop Shop? We've never seen you in here before and where's your uniform?"

"I took it off for the last time this afternoon. I'm on pension."

We still were in the process of congratulating Mr. Conklin when the barmaid, Eileen O'Conner, appeared with a tray of suds for us and double whiskey for the Mr. Conklin.

"Boys," he said," here's to you and all the pleasure you gave me while you were growing up. I'm going to miss you boys of all the people I stopped and questioned over the years. Down the hatch and good luck to you next hunting season."

We all thanked him, but Spunky had a funny look in his eyes.

"You're putting us on," Spunky said. "How many times have you stopped us and searched our truck looking for illegal game or more than our limit of fish? Too many to count, I'd bet."

"A hundred and seventeen," the old coot said. "I looked it up before I came to town."

"And you never found anything," Spunky said.

"Well, I didn't write any tickets or take you in, but that doesn't mean I never found anything."

"Like what?"

"The doe you took to the Schwartz family for one. And there's other times. I always knew what you boys were up to, but I figured not to bother you as long as it was for charity."

We sat stunned at the coot's words —Spunky particularly because it was always his idea to help a neighbor who was out of work or had too many kids to feed on his earnings.

Mr. Conklin spent an hour telling stories about our gang that we thought only the big man in the sky could know.

Always the pragmatist, Spunky asked who was going to replace him as game warden?

"Conservation Officer," the coot said. "I don't know his name, but they tell me he's an aggressive fellow. That's why I came down here tonight. I know that you've been straight since you matured, but I thought I'd let you know it won't be me looking over your shoulder from now on."

A nice looking woman came to the table as Mr. Conklin was speaking. She tapped him on the shoulder and told him his ride had arrived.

"My wife," Mr.Conklin said.

We all shook hands with Mr. Conklin and wished him luck in retirement.

We met the new conservation officer about a month later during the bow season for deer. Spunky and I had just turned off a two-track onto a county road when a pair of headlights under a pair of blue flashing lights loomed up behind us.

Spunky pulled onto the shoulder of the road and a big uniformed figure approached the driver's window.

"What you fellas up to," a voice barked.

"Been deer hunting," Spunky said.

"Hunting kind of late, aren't you? Legal shooting was an hour ago."

"My friend got turned around and I had to wait for him."

"May I see some identification?"

The officer took the papers back to his car. He was gone a long time.

"Do you mind if I look inside of the truck's cap?" he asked. "And stay in the truck, please."

We could hear him rummaging in the back and Spunky asked if I knew why the guy had his dander up.

Everything looks okay," a voice said at the passenger window said 15 minutes later.

"Tom Conklin told me he suspected a group of poachers have been working this area. When I saw the ID that the name was Spriggs it rang a bell and I had to check it out.

"The coot — er, Mr. Conklin — told you about me?" Spunky said.

"No, but I remember there was a guy named Spriggs who made my life miserable all through high school — kept calling me 'Dink' every chance he had.

What followed in the next half hour was the most unique reunion ever held in our neck of the woods."

The Price of Friendship

It was 10:30 at night. I had just settled into my bed when the phone on the night stand rang. I jerked to a sitting position and felt the hitch in my back as I reached for the phone.

'Hello," I grumbled.

"Herb, it's Dee. Spunky fell from the loft in the barn and broke both of his wrists," Spunky's wife said in one breath. "Can you come to hospital and help me get him home?"

"Be right there," I told her.

"Bring your car, not the truck," Dee said. "I don't think he is able to climb into a truck."

"What's the matter?" my wife asked.

"Poor Spunky. He's broken both of his wrists. I've got to help get him home from the hospital."

"Poor Dee," my wife said as she rolled over.

It wasn't raining. It was teeming. The rain was slanting against the windshield and it took me more than 30 minutes to get to the hospital 20 miles from home. Spunky, Dee and a nurse were waiting at the emergency door.

I saw the two casts when I opened the passenger door. Spunky looked like a mummy I had seen in a movie when I was a kid. He didn't say anything as the nurse bent him into the front seat.

"Don't forget to take a pain pill before you go to bed and remember keep the arms elevated until you come back to see the doctor. Good Luck," the nurse called as she slammed the door shut.

Spunky was silent on most of the ride home. Dee told me he had been up in the barn loft getting his deer hunting gear together when he slipped on some damp straw and fell 15 feet to the cement floor.

"That's all he has to know," Spunky growled at his wife.

It took some time and a lot of #x@/x#s to get Spunky out of the car and into the house and I didn't get home until 2 a.m.

My wife had gotten up and was waiting for me. She began grilling me on Spunky's accident and injuries. I described the accident and repeated Spunky's — "that's all he has to know" — warning and went to bed.

First thing after breakfast I went to see Spunky and to ask if there was anything I could do to help. I heard loud voices coming from the house before I opened the car door and honked the horn to warn them of my arrival.

Dee opened the door and I saw a glum Spunky sitting at the table in his bathrobe, both elbows resting on the table and the two casts on the lower parts of his arm standing upright like goal posts on a football field.

"I'm glad you came," Spunky said. "You probably prevented a murder."

"You exaggerate. You wouldn't hurt Dee for anything."

"You got it wrong, with these damn casts, I was going to be the victim."

"He says he's going deer hunting with you guys in 10 days, and I told him there was no way in hell he was going to be able to hunt."

I told Spunky I thought Dee was right and that there was no possible way he could hunt with us this year.

"Where there's a will there's a way," came Spunky's reply. "And if you're going to side with my wife, good-bye."

Two days later the gang held an emergency meeting at the Slop Shop to discuss the hunt and wrap up final details of who would bring what. We had just about figured who was bringing and doing what when Dee and Spunky walked in.

"Hi," he said in greeting. "I called Herb's place and Mary told me you were here finalizing the deer hunt. Well, count me in."

"Great," I said, "but how are you going to hunt or pull the trigger, with casts from your elbows to your wrists."

Spunky showed us where he had whittled down the cast on his right wrist and assured us that he could stand the pain while he pulled the trigger.

"In fact, I fired one shot this afternoon — in the black at 50 yards."

"Okay, you can shoot," Brad Morrison said, "but how are you going to do the other stuff alone. Stuff like being able to feed yourself, getting yourself dressed and things like that."

"Well, I've been thinking on that and have put together a list of the things that I need to have done for me. I've also chosen the one who will be assigned to that task each day. I will limit myself to a three-day hunt.

"I'm going to leave the list with you and you can decide whether or not you want me to hunt with you. I left Fast Eddie Bresler off the list, because he doesn't know me as much as the rest of you do."

With that Spunky stood up and walked to the back door. Dee joined him immediately and they left.

Skip Fisher reached over and grabbed the list. He looked at the rest of us: "I didn't know that he can't get the zipper up or down by himself or that he isn't able to wash or wipe himself after. . . after . . . a . . . a . . . BM. Maybe we ought to break our all male tradition and invite Dee to hunt with us.

It was a long meeting and it wasn't until 15 minutes before last call that the gang called for a secret ballot that took a two-thirds majority to carry — one way or the other. Before voting we revised the week's menu striking such favorites as chili, baked beans and hot salami.

We asked Fast Eddie to count the ballots. It seemed like it took him a long time to count the ballots but eventually he said: "Spunky means a lot to me. He has sort of been my mentor and I'm happy that I will get to hunt with him again this year. You all must feel that way. The vote is one hundred percent in favor of Spunky hunting with us."

Trout Lily

No Matinee Idol

Clark Gable began making movies in the 1930's and was a matinee idol for at least three decades. Women fawned over the handsome Hollywood actor and Gable had his share of male fans, even if it was because he always got his woman.

Even I, who might be described as a non-movie goer, remember his closing line in "Gone With The Wind" in which he turned to Vivian Leigh playing the role of Scarlett O'Hara and said: "Frankly my dear, I don't give a damn."

That was a shocking line at the time and there was much conversation about the movie in our town. News didn't travel as fast in those days, but we heard about the line within a week. I write about the movie and Clark Gable because they were the reason many youngsters in our town picked a matinee idol.

Not that any of us would call Spunky Spriggs a matinee idol to his face, but we all regarded him with what might be considered childish enthusiasm. Everyone wanted to be his friend. They were in awe of him. They followed him around school, sat near him at lunch and wanted to spend time with him at recess. No one, however, asked to copy his homework.

It was a child's fad and passed in no time. Spunky, while the most proficient hunter, trapper and fisherman in our class, was never an idol for members of the gang while we were in school. He didn't become even a quasi-idol until later.

We were out of school long enough to go back to our 25th Class Reunion before we realized that Spunky was an idol and it was all Fast Eddie Bresler's fault. The change in classification came slowly. Fast Eddie had moved from Florida to teach science in the local high school. He happened to rent the farm house next to Spunky's. That's how idols are made.

Whenever Fast Eddie ran into trouble with his lawnmower, car or vegetable garden, he always asked Spunky for advice. The advice usually ended with Spunky fixing whatever. Spunky didn't seem to mind, and, in fact, he reveled in it. Maybe that's why he asked Fast Eddie to go ice fishing with us the first winter he lived in our town.

Fast Eddie watched everything Spunky did. After a couple of years he even began to walk like Spunky — the first of many Spunky feats he tried to emulate.

At Fast Eddie's first deer camp, for instance, he watched as Spunky piled the wood for the camp fire and stood back to watch him light the fire.

Spunky always made a big thing of starting the fire shortly after we were in camp. He wouldn't let any of his old friends help. He prided himself on getting the campfire going, cooling it off and bringing it back to life the next night after hunting.

Brad Morrison happened to be passing the fire pit when Spunky was giving Fast Eddie a lesson in fire starting. He stopped to listen.

Brad told the rest of the gang the lesson on fire starting went something like this.

"You got to start with a big pit, lots of wood and a can of kerosene if you want a fire that you can restart any time you want," Spunky told Fast Eddie. "This is how I layer the wood so that the embers will be gathered in one place and retain some heat for a long time.

"Let's say it is opening morning. The fire looks dead, but way down at the bottom it still has enough heat and unburned edges of the old wood to ignite the new wood we just heaped on top."

"I watched you and that's what I have been doing at home," Fast Eddie said. "I pile on the wood just as you have, but it never ignites."

Morrison said Spunky looked around to see if anyone of the gang was within hearing distance.

"I give it a couple of dashes of kerosene and bingo the whole pile begins to burn in short order."

"Thanks Spunky," Fast Eddie said just before Brad slipped out from behind the tree he had used for cover.

Skip Fisher and I told Brad that Spunky was just funnin' with Fast Eddie. The lessons continued for three or four hunting seasons and we stayed out of it, but Fast Eddie was at his idol's side during the annual fire lighting ceremony,

Years passed and we all more or less forgot about the conversation, until Skip stopped by the house about midnight one Fall. He was dressed in his Volunteer Fireman's regalia.

"I seen the light," he said from the porch. "How about a cup of coffee for a tired puppy?"

"I can do better than that. You look beat."

"I'll have both. I am beat. We had a barn fire."

"Who's place?"

"Fast Eddie's. The darn fool was having some of the teachers at the school over for a cookout at a pit he dug too close to the barn. I guess he was showing off some of that stuff he picked up from Spunky during the hunting seasons. He had lit a fire yesterday.

"Anyway there was no fire going when the guests arrived because he wanted to show them how quickly he could get it roaring. He took them to the pit, and according to the principal Fast Eddie said 'watch this'.

Skip said he dashed some kerosene on the pit the way Spunky did it, but must have used a tad more dashes of kerosene. The next thing he knew the teachers are screaming and running away from the barn. It was lucky no one got hurt but the barn is gone. It was the worst barn fire I ever saw.

"I never seen Fast Eddie look so sad, but the principal told me it was the most exciting evening of his life."

Skunk Cabbage.

The Big Splash

The light was barely visible when Skip Fisher parked his van in a parking spot near the mouth of the Pere Marquette at Ludington one Fall and the gang,minus Spunky Spriggs trudged through the sand to reach the beginning of the dock.

Brad Morrison and I carried a large cooler and Skip and Fast Eddie Bresler another cooler out to an open spot on the concrete pier. It was cool, not cold, but Fast Eddie, a transplant from Florida, was bundled up like he was in Alaska. In fact he looked like an Eskimo boy.

We had agreed we each would fish with a different colored spoon and when one of us caught a fish or had a hit, we all would switch to that color and make a killing. We would be casting downwind and the spoons would sail a mile.

We labored for two hours without a hit and I was watching to see if anyone along the long concrete pier was having any luck.

"I'm going to take a walk out to the end and see if anyone is doing any good," I said, and put my rod down, relieved to give my right arm a rest. "It will take me a little time, so keep my spot open," I said. "this is near where Spunky killed them last year."

"I hope he's having a good time at his father-in-laws birthday party," Brad said. "It sure doesn't feel like fishing without Spunky being here."

"Yeah, and we aren't catching any fish," Skip lamented. "From reports I thought it would be a snap to fill our limits. Just once I'd like to catch a good stringer when Spunky wasn't here. I thought they was going to hit for sure."

"You really are trying to show Spunky up, but ease up. The fish can feel your panic," I said before I walked away.

I was gone 10 minutes and at 100 yards away from the group I could see the grin on Fast Eddie's face. I didn't ask did ya? I asked how big?

"Skip hung him on his scale and says he is a tad under 17 pounds. Want to see 'em?"

"Sure."

Fast Eddie reached down and pulled up a lengthy piece of clothes line at the end of which hung a beautiful chinook or king if you prefer. It was thrashing so wildly that Fast Eddie threw the line into the water and began trying to get the slime off of his pant leg.

"He's frisky. How old's the clothesline?"

"Not too old to keep my salmon under control."

We fished until it got too dark to see before heading for a motel where we cleaned the fish and packed it in ice in one of the coolers before going out to dinner.

Fast Eddie was a fast talker during dinner and described the fight he had with the salmon because I wasn't there when he caught it.

We were out of motel early, had breakfast at a small restaurant and headed back for the pier. There was an intermittent drizzle falling as we walked out onto the pier in our rain garb.

"I hate fishing in the rain," I said, more to myself than anyone.

"Spunky says that fish hit good in the rain. He says the fish bite because they don't think any human will be out trying to kill him.

"What else did Spunky tell you?" I asked.

"He told me not to cast and just reel. He said to let the bait stop occasionally and then jerk it ahead quickly because sometimes a fish will hit because it thinks the lure saw him and was trying to get away.

"I told you last night that the fish hit just after I had jerked it."

I had just turned away to make my first cast when Fast Eddie's voice broke the silence: "Fish On," he yelled.

I laid my rod down and coached Fast Eddie on how to play the fish. He apparently didn't hear me because all he did was hold onto the rod and let the fish run. Finally it stopped and Fast Eddie started to pump the fish back to the dock

Fifteen minutes later Fast Eddie tied it to his stringer and lowered it into the water.

Brad and I hooked fish at the exact same second and both of them threw the hook on their first jump.

Fast Eddie said something about "that's the way it goes sometime," and made his second cast of the morning.

"Fish On," he yelled after turning the reel handle two turns.

Again it took him forever to lead the fish to the net — another chinook about the same size."

"Wow, it's my day," he said while lowering his two fish into the water on the clothesline.

"My arms are tired. I think I'll watch a few minutes before casting again."

Skip managed a smaller chinook late in the morning. Skip and I were still skunked. About 11 a.m. we ate the sandwiches that we had purchased at the restaurant during breakfast.

Fast Eddie, who does everything fast picked up his rod, and made a cast while the three of us were finishing our lunch.

"Herb, I left the spoon I've been using for you," Fast Eddie said. "I hope it will bring you some luck."

Thanks," I said.

'Fish on," Fast Eddie shouted.

None of us got up. We knew it would take forever for Fast Eddie to land the fish. We sat finishing out lunch and watched the battle.

"He's tired," Fast Eddie said.

Skip got up and netted the fish. He swung it up on the dock and said: "It's a little bigger than the first two."

I had just gotten to my feet when Fast Eddie lifted his stringer of fish over the water as I turned to make my first cast. I heard a loud splash and there was Fast Eddie in the water wrestling with something.

Seconds later he stood — up to his chest — struggling with the end of the clothesline.

"Put a net down," he shouted. "I'll put a fish in the net and you all put it on the dock.

It took some time to get all three fish onto the dock and for Brad to attach them to his stringer. In fact it took long enough so that a rescue boat came out of the basin behind the dock and reached Fast Eddie just the last fish was hooked onto the chain stringer.

"We'll meet at the van," I shouted as Fast Eddie was pulled away from the dock.

We gathered all of our gear and were almost to the end of the dock when Fast Eddie got there. At the van Fast Eddie took a set of dry clothes from his suitcase and changed in the backseat.

He emerged in dry clothes and a blanket that was on the front seat around his shoulders. His teeth continued to make clicking noises, but he spoke clearly when he said: "Sorry guys."

We went to a coffee shop and watched Fast Eddie horse down two cups of hot coffee. He put the cup on the counter and looked at us.

"What happened?" we all asked at once.

"I'm ashamed to tell you, but I think Herb knows."

'This morning when I saw the line he was using after if he caught the first fish," I began. "It looked to be in bad shape, frayed almost the whole length and I asked him if it was strong enough. He assured me it was.

"I think it would have lasted the day if he hadn't caught so many fish. I'd also bet it held up until he got the heavy load over the dock and began lowering it.

"He just caught too many fish for the rope, but don't ask me why he jumped in after them. He'll have to answer that himself."

"When the rope broke, I saw that the fish were still attached," Fast Eddie said. "I didn't consciously think that, but I wasn't going to let the best catch I ever made get away and jumped in and grabbed the rope."

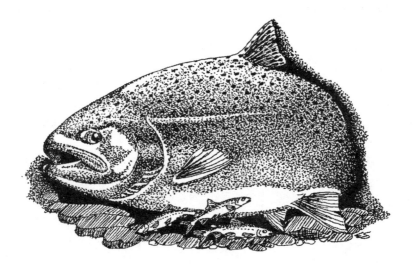

The Climber

The telling of "war stories" dates back to biblical times. The language was different thousands of years ago, but the gist of the stories about personal heroics, great and not so great generals, and cowardice has remained pretty much the same to this day.

As kids, the gang used to hang onto every word our fathers spoke about the first Big War. They always were into the best stories about the time the ladies convinced their husbands that it was time to go home.

"The party is over," is the way I remember them saying it.

All of the gang saw service in Europe during World War II except me. I went to the Pacific and ended up in China. Spunky Spriggs attributes it to the fact he always thought I was different.

Fast Eddie Bresler, a late comer to the gang and more than a score of years younger than the rest of us, keeps badgering the gang to tell him about our service time. We usually demurred, and Fast Eddie, who looks upon the gang as his heroes, would become quiet and withdrawn when we refused.

In fact, he downright sulked until one of us told a short war story. That made Fast Eddie happy and he would buy an extra round in his excitement.

Now the gang isn't about to let a free round pass. So on meeting nights we always chose someone in advance to tell a war story — if Fast Eddie insisted. It was an hour before closing one night when it was my turn to buy the next round.

"Who's going to tell us about something when you were in service?" he asked.

We looked at each other for a few seconds before I said, "Okay."

"Let's have a round," Fast Eddie called to the barmaid. "On me."

I waited until the drinks were served before I began.

"You ever see me atop the barn?" I asked Fast Eddie.

"Sure."

"No you didn't. Herb doesn't like heights," Brad Morrison piped up.

"What's that got to do with the war" from Fast Eddie.

"Let Herb tell you about his act of bravery."

"It's no secret around here that I don't like to climb, but with my Marine buddies I was a climbing fool. In fact I had a reputation as a gung-ho climber. It all happened while I was with the 3rd Corps Headquarters unit in Tientsin.

"Back in those we didn't have radios like they have today and at headquarters when a phone line went down it was like a four alarm fire. If you were on duty, you scrambled to get communication between us and whatever unit couldn't be reached during a routine communications checks.

"If communications between units were interrupted, you fixed it, pronto. We were fixing lines all of the time because Chinese entrepreneurs, almost every night, cut lines for metal they used to make souvenirs for the Marines to buy and send to their girlfriends.

"That wasn't too bad. Maybe it was because it was dark and from atop a 15-foot pole the ground didn't look so menacing. My problems were at the tower.

"I was the new man on the squad when I first visited the tower. It was a square pole — four inches to a side — and looked tall enough to bump low clouds. Every time there was a storm of any kind, the squad would have to check the connections at the top to insure uninterrupted communications with distant units scattered around the area.

"As the new man, it was my turn to climb. The leader gave me an instruction book on everything I had to accomplish at the top. He told me it was something they did every time a storm passed through the area.

"I surprised myself and made it to the top in decent time and secured my belt. (Marines don't climb with belts.) Of course, I had to look down to accomplish this and I nearly pulled my gaffs out of the pole.

"That one look took away any desire I had to climb, but I had to get down and the only way to accomplish this was to check the connections first. I knew from classes that it's hard to work around a square pole, especially one with smooth and sawed sides, but I made two circles around the pole and checked the connections out in proper order.

"Climbing down you look down to make sure your gaffs take a good bite. You lay your weight into them to make sure they will hold before taking the upper gaff out of the pole. Well, I made it about a third of the way down before I started to get jittery.

"Getting jittery is a bad thing and I swung the rope around my waist and rested against the pole, filled and lit my pipe and reported to those on the ground how beautiful the scenery was from this height. I smoked half a pipe before calming down enough to go another third of the way.

"When I stopped again the squad leader cussed me out for real. I held my spot until I felt right and the climb ended safely, but I wasn't looking forward to the next time.

"The next time my name was on the top of the list the squad leader sent someone else up because he had a date with a pretty Navy nurse. If I send you up I'll never make it on time. I was transferred out of the unit two months later with the reputation as the nutty guy who liked it up high."

"That's it?" Fast Eddie questioned. "You really were scared of heights?"

"Nah, not really, just shaky enough to keep me on the ground."